# FEVER

## A Story from a Devon Churchyard

GW00393235

*By the same author*

THE MEMORY BE GREEN; AN ORAL HISTORY OF
A DEVON VILLAGE

# FEVER

## A Story from a Devon Churchyard

Liz Shakespeare

LETTERBOX BOOKS

First published 2005
by
Letterbox Books
Littleham
Bideford
Devon
EX39 5HW

Copyright © Liz Shakespeare 2005
All rights reserved

ISBN 0-9516879-1-3
978-0-9516879-1-8

Printed and bound by SRP Ltd, Exeter.

# ACKNOWLEDGEMENTS

I would like to thank the staff of the North Devon Local Studies Library and Record Office; Peter Christie; Shirley Cowling, Alison Harding, Mary Maher and Nora Bendle for their advice and encouragement; Kate Cryan for her careful reading; Ben for all his hard work.

Thanks also to Dr Gregory Stevens Cox for permission to reproduce the nineteenth century photograph incorporated in the cover design.

# CONTENTS

Alternate chapters are research and *imaginative reconstruction.*

Map of Littleham, 1871.
Prologue                                          1
*Tuesday 29th November 1870*                      3
Chapter One                                      19
*Wednesday 14th December 1870*                   27
Chapter Two                                      45
*Saturday 31st December 1870*                    63
Chapter Three                                    77
*Thursday 19th January 1871*                     91
Chapter Four                                    105
*The Diary Of James Andrew (1)*                 125
Chapter Five                                    145
*The Diary of James Andrew (2)*                 161
Chapter Six                                     177
*Sunday 19th March 1871*                        197
Chapter Seven                                   213
*Friday 7th April 1871*                         225
Chapter Eight                                   237
Epilogue                                        257
Bibliography                                    259

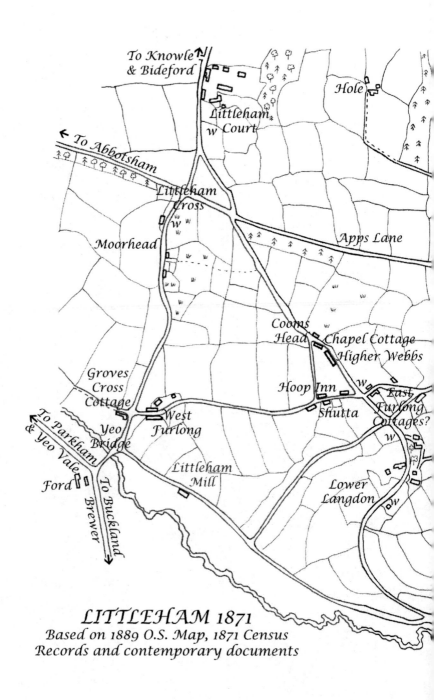

To Knowle
& Bideford

Hole

Littleham
*w* Court

← To Abbotsham

Littleham
Cross

Apps Lane

*w*

Moorhead

Cooms
Head

Chapel Cottage
Higher Webbs

Hoop Inn

*w*

East
Turlong
Cottages?

Groves
Cross
Cottage

West
Turlong

Shutta

*w*

Yeo
Bridge

To Parkham
& Yeo Vale

Littleham
Mill

Lower
Langdon

Ford

To Buckland
Brewer

## LITTLEHAM 1871
Based on 1889 O.S. Map, 1871 Census
Records and contemporary documents

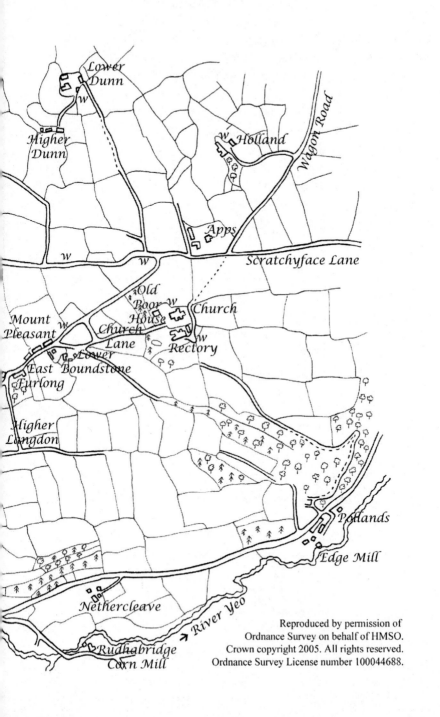

Lower
Dunn
w
Higher
Dunn
w Holland
Wagon Road
Apps
w
w W Scratchyface Lane
Old
Poor w
House Church
Mount w
Pleasant Church
Lane
Lower
East Boundstone
Furlong
Rectory
w
Higher
Langdon
Pollands
Edge Mill
Nethercleave
River Yeo
Rudhabridge
Corn Mill

Reproduced by permission of
Ordnance Survey on behalf of HMSO.
Crown copyright 2005. All rights reserved.
Ordnance Survey License number 100044688.

# PROLOGUE

The harsh words were cut deep into the cold stone. The severity of the message was undiminished even though the passing of time had allowed sage green lichen and tendrils of ivy to soften the edges of the headstone and flowering grasses to grow about its base. I shivered despite the warmth of the morning sun on my back. A father aged 33 years and his three young daughters. All four had died within a few weeks. The date seemed somehow familiar and I frowned in concentration. February 1871. I straightened up and looked around.

The churchyard in Littleham, North Devon is set on the side of a hill and enclosed by trees. The headstones seem to gather about the small, rugged fifteenth century church that huddles in the middle. Whereas most local churches are set on hilltops to declare their whereabouts, Littleham's tower is hidden from view until one turns the final corner of the high-banked lane from the village. Its secretive location gives the churchyard a particular air of seclusion and peace. Only the occasional drone of a tractor disturbing the birdsong reminds us that we are in the twenty-first century, for the church is too distant from a main road for any traffic noise to be heard. Like many rural churchyards it is the last vestige of unadulterated pasture amidst improved farmland, the grass between the graves only being cut in early summer when many of the wild plants have already flowered. In January the grass under the old yew tree is white with snowdrops, later come early purple orchids, huge clumps of primroses and violets in the hedge banks and wild daffodils and bluebells amongst the graves.

I lived in the village of Littleham and passed through the churchyard most days while out for a walk, for it is crossed by a public footpath that links old tracks and woodland paths. Like most people I glanced at the headstones as I passed and those alongside the path grew familiar, like the faces of old friends. Here and there a name gathered greater significance; this one was familiar through reading the deeds of my house; that one bore a name still to be found in the village today. It was not until I wandered off the path one day that I noticed the memorial to the father and his three daughters.

1871. Why was the date familiar? I stood very still and tried to remember. Then I walked back towards the path. There it was. An insignificant stone bearing the name of a small girl who had died on 10th April 1871. From there I searched on and found more graves, all dating from the first half of 1871, most of them of children. I continued on my walk in a subdued frame of mind. Of course we know that child mortality was high in the nineteenth century, that childhood diseases which now cause a few days' discomfort were then killers, for the story is told in every graveyard in England. But I felt that I knew some of these people; that I lived not only in the village of today but connected by imagination to the village of the past, and I began to wonder how so many deaths in a short time would have affected this small community. Who were the parents and grandparents of that small girl? Who was the woman who lost her husband and three daughters within a few weeks?

# Tuesday 29th November 1870

Ann Williams surreptitiously stretches her aching back, moving slowly so that the bench does not creak, and wriggles her toes where the hard corrugations of her stiff leather boots dig into them. Keeping her head still, she raises her eyes from her slate and watches Mrs Sing as she pushes a pile of chopped potatoes from a plate into the pan that hangs over the fire in the black hollow of the hearth. Ann has no idea what the time is and, even had there been a clock in the room, would have been unable to read its hands, but the ritual of the potatoes is as good as a clock and she resists an impulse to leap up at the thought of the long day finally drawing to a close. She gives her younger brother John a swift kick to rouse him from his dream and sets her pencil squeaking on her slate again as she finishes copying the last word of the sentence that she has now written six times. As Mrs Sing replaces the lid on the pot, she turns and orders in a reedy voice,

"Class, put your pencils down".

Ann waits impatiently while the small fragile body in her layers of black clothes moves steadily along the line of children, giving a sharp word of criticism here, a nod of approbation there. There are twenty-eight children in the room, sixteen seated on the forms facing the fireplace and twelve babies, who are taught by Mrs Sing's daughter, Sophia Bartlett, facing the opposite wall. There is more than twice this number on the school roll but most children only come when their parents can spare the weekly penny fee and when they are not needed for jobs at home. Ann would not be here herself if Mr Heywood, her father's employer, had not already paid her penny. She wishes he had not done so. He does not seem to realise how difficult things are for her mother while

3

the little ones are ill, and one more week off school would surely not have mattered.

Mrs Sing leans over Ann's shoulder and nods at the elaborate curlicues decorating the slate.

"Good. Read it."

Ann recognises the first letter on the slate as being the same as that in her family name and forms her lips optimistically into a pucker. After a long pause Mrs Sing snaps,

"Wanton actions are very unseemly."

"Yes Miss".

"You'm eleven years old. You should be reading, Ann."

"Yes, Mrs Sing".

John, being two years younger, gets away with having a finger stabbing at his most crooked letters and soon the order comes to wipe the slates clean. Sixteen mouths spit with accuracy and sixteen sleeves, universal wipers of noses and slates, are brought into action. The babies, who have been chanting numbers, are ordered to turn around on their benches so that all face the fireplace and a final prayer is said.

Ann quickly buttons some of the little ones into their jackets while John and the other bigger boys stack the benches with practised speed against the end wall of the long, low room. A large deal table, complete with the utensils Mary Sing used to prepare her supper, is then carried into the centre and three chairs placed around it, thus returning the space to its evening function and rendering it almost indistinguishable from any other cottage room. As the children leave the two women set about their afternoon chores in readiness for the return of Sylvia's husband.

Cooms Head, the cottage that doubles as a school for children of Wesleyan Methodists, is set on the edge of the North Devon village of Littleham. The chapel itself, consisting of a room attached to another dwelling, stands a few yards away on the hill leading down into the village and it is in this direction that most of the children set off. Ann and John, however, turn up the hill to begin their half-mile walk to the cottage at Littleham Court Farm where their father works as a farm labourer. It is a mild, drizzly day with a strong south-westerly and John reacts in the way of many young animals when out in a high wind by kicking up his heels, a trick that proves particularly entertaining as his left boot, its lace having gone missing some days previously, flies off and lands in the hedge. Roaring with exaggerated laughter he pulls on his boot again and hops wildly on one leg, his cut-down, patched and now outgrown trousers flapping just below his knees, until he manages to launch his boot into space once more.

Ann ignores him and pushes on up the hill, head down against the wind and one hand clutching the square of blanket that serves as a shawl around her. She tries to push her anxieties aside. The baby is well and Mary-Jane had seemed a little happier that morning, had even smiled when Ann waved goodbye to her. Perhaps William too will be playing on the mat when she gets home. As she walks she keeps her eyes on the hedgebank, searching with seasoned discrimination for late dandelions and sow thistles to take home for the pig. The wind whips a few last beech leaves from the top of the six foot high bank and Ann turns sharply and watches as John runs back down the lane to leap high and catch one deftly with a joyous whoop. They both laugh out loud at the prospect of the good luck the caught leaf will bring and Ann's optimism increases. As they approach the brow of the hill she pauses at a boggy piece of ground at the base of the hedge and calls to her brother, now progressing up the slope in giant leaps.

"John, mind the pig. There be master long grass yur."

Together they pick armfuls of the lush grass and run down the hill towards their home, scattering chickens that peck in the verges.

The horned Red Devon cattle are already in the yard, standing patiently chewing the cud while they wait to be milked. As the children push through them, John slapping their hindquarters and shouting, to reach the pigsty that lies below the two farm cottages, their father appears from the shippon, wiping his hands on the sack that is tied round his waist. He wears a cap pushed to the back of his head, revealing a thin, drawn face and small eyes grown cold through hardship.

"Get on 'oom quickly, yer mother needs you."

Ann stares at him for a moment then hurries down to the sty, her face set. The pig greets them with short impatient grunts, his long snout reaching over the wall and quivering with anticipation. Today they do not stop to tease him with blades of grass but throw the leaves and grass over into the trough, hurry round to the cottage door and lift the latch with a clatter.

They burst into the small dim room which, now that there is little daylight left to penetrate the one small window, is lit only by the gleam of a dying fire. Their neighbour John Westcott sits stooped on a low stool by the fireplace that forms the end wall of the room, a young baby crying weakly on his lap and a small girl, little more than a baby herself, playing on the rag rug at his feet. He raises his sightless eyes questioningly towards the door and Ann shouts,

"'Tis only us, Uncl' John."

She crosses the room quickly and bends to take the baby from his arms while shouting again, "'Tis Ann and John".

"Aahh". He relinquishes his hold on the baby and reaches out a hand to check on the small girl who is now pulling herself up to stand at his knee, the tiny hand clutching the top of his leather gaiters.

He is a small, wizened man, barely taller than Ann herself and bent by years of carrying sacks of coal, a task he performed to the wonderment of onlookers with one hand supporting the sack and the other holding out an oak staff to feel what he could not see. At fifty-seven he is now too old and frail to carry out any but the most simple tasks for Ann's family or her grandparents with whom he boards in the adjoining cottage. He turns his face now towards Ann but she is busy rocking the baby and coaxing it back to acquiescence with her finger that is sucked vigorously. She straightens its bonnet, which has turned almost obscuring its face, and addresses her brother who is still at the door.

"Get een some logs and make up the fire, then make sure there's water in the kettle."

"Where's mother?"

"William must be bad. Get on, hurry." She turns towards the door which opens on to the stairs and the blind man, feeling no reassuring touch of response to his questioning glance, turns back to the small child tugging at his breeches.

Ann creeps up the bare wooden stairs so that her nailed boots do not make a noise and emerges into the room that she shares with her little sister and two brothers. Her mother, kneeling by the side of one of the straw mattresses that are ranged on the floor, raises her thin, tired face in relief. Ann hands her the baby and she unbuttons her dress with her free hand.

"Thank the Lord you're back. 'E's bad again, I've hardly been able to leave'n be all day. Is the fire out?" Ann shakes her head. "Well, that's a blessing. And he's gone off now."

Ann crouches down to her little brother and brushes the tousled hair from his hot little face. His open mouth twitches a little. She looks into her mother's eyes and sees the fear that is mirrored in her own.

"'Tis like Henry was."

"Henry was younger. William's a strong lad." The words are said without feeling and are not convincing. Ann can remember Henry's death clearly although she was only five years old herself, a year older than William is now. Another memory comes back to her, one that seems to have no beginning and no precise end but which forms a chasm in her childhood. She remembers bursting into the cottage for a slice of bread and lard after long mornings spent building dams of mud and sticks across the stream, to find her mother still sitting at the table, silent among the breakfast things. She did not always answer when Ann called out to her and looked at her daughter as if she was not there, yet stared at blank walls as if she could see things invisible to Ann herself. The memory of that time makes her feel cold and alone even now.

She watches as her mother sits back on a mattress to feed the baby and she frowns with concentration.

"Us could give'n some tea, put in some onions p'raps. I could make it."

Her mother nods without looking up.

"I could sit with'n, tell'n a story like the minister do."

"If he wakes you could sit with'n."

Ann looks down at the flushed face on the pillow and her longing for normality is so strong that she wants to leap up and shout with frustration. "Us gave Mary-Jane onion tea, her's up now, it worked for she."

Her mother shifts the baby on to her shoulder and smiles sadly at Ann. "You'm a good girl. Make some onion gruel while I get the tea, then there's gloves to finish. Mrs Hearn comes tomorrow and I've done nought today." The mother glances anxiously towards the tiny window. "'Tis getting dimmity and there be a whole pair to finish."

"I'll do'm, us mustn't lose the two shilling." Ann pictures the coins that will be handed over for the gloves, she loves to hold them and know that her work has helped to earn them. She jumps up. "I'll give Mary-Jane some more gruel too, make sure her's better."

Later that evening Ann crouches on a stool by the fireplace, bending her head low over the leather glove she is sewing in an effort to make the tiny stitches of uniform length. Her mother has pulled her hair back tightly so that stray hairs do not get sewn into the fine needlework, and the dim light cast by a candle set on another stool close by throws dark shadows on her thin face. Her parents went to bed some half an hour ago, soon after the younger children, and the creaking and rustling from upstairs ceased very quickly as all fell into an exhausted sleep. Ann can just hear the crackling of the fire and occasional whimpering which she knows to be William. He was carried downstairs for a while this evening to lie crying plaintively in the arms of his grandmother who came from her cottage next door to help. Ann watched her calmly taking control, loosening William's clothing and wrapping cold damp cloths round his burning throat with practised ease. He took a few mouthfuls of onion tea but cried at each swallow and soon turned his face from the cup. As the evening wore on, the reassuring litany of, "*C'mon* old chap, *c'mon,* you'll be better dreckly," died away and Ann saw furrows developing on her grandmother's already lined brow.

She and her mother always try to finish the gloves before sunset, as it is very hard to produce neat enough work by candlelight. Once, the pack woman, Mrs Hearn, threw a pair of gloves into the farmyard mud when she saw the stitches and her mother had to give money for the leather instead of being paid. She turns the glove a little more towards the light and pushes the needle back through the leather a hair's breadth from her last stitch. They are ladies' long gloves in fine, pale grey leather, decorated with lines of stitching on the backs. She is only half way through this second one. She looks up at the empty chair where her mother sits when they work together. It is going to be a long night.

By the middle of the next morning she is on her way to the village with Mary-Jane. She has sat upstairs with William and minded the two youngest children while John was ordered out to the yard to chop wood and her mother set about baking bread with sleeves pushed up to her elbows and her lips tightly pressed. Ann struggled to keep the two little ones amused in the bare, draughty room by telling them rhymes and bouncing the baby on her lap. William was quieter today but when Ann had said he must be a little better, her mother had merely said she would rather hear him cry. Every now and then she came upstairs and placed a floury hand on his forehead and Ann watched as he closed his eyes to let her, his pale lids forming perfect half moons above his dark lashes. When he opened his eyes again they were wide and dark and unfocussed, as if the room and his mother were not there.

Ann is going now to the shop to buy a twist of tea and to see if anyone has some Holloway's Ointment. "You'm not to ask now, mind, but it may be that some will be offered if folks see you about." Holloway's Ointment is expensive, 1s 2d a pot, but people say it can cure anything from sore throats to old sores and stiff joints. Ann reaches the brow of the hill and shifts Mary-Jane on to her left hip. Baby Richard is asleep at home and William quiet so she has been able to leave them, but Mary-Jane would have got under her mother's feet. As she approaches the school she can hear a hum of voices which, as she draws nearer, forms itself into a chant. She stands outside and listens as Mrs Sing's voice cuts through, then the reassuring chant begins again, rising and falling in familiar cadences. Mary-Jane points at the cottage door with a questioning, "Er?"

"School".

"Sool," she repeats, satisfied, and replaces her thumb in her mouth. Ann imagines her friend Elizabeth Palmer sitting in her usual place. It seems strange now that when they are in there, they so often wish to be out. She shivers as a sudden gust of wind tugs at her bonnet and she continues down the road to the village.

There are two shops in the village; the better-stocked one run by the widowed mother of two children is opposite East Furlong Farm and the other, run by a very old lady known as Gran Hookaway, further on in a tiny cottage in the row called Mount Pleasant. Ann hesitates in the road by the first shop. So far she has seen no one but farm workers and the carpenter at Higher Webbs and she knows she has to see a sympathetic woman, perhaps one of her cousins, if she is to have any chance of being given some ointment, so she carries on up the road towards Mount Pleasant. She pauses outside the first cottage where her friend Mary Powe and her brother and two sisters live. They all go to the church school held in a room in the Rectory and as their father works as a groom for the Rector, the children are expected to set a good example by going to school most days. The cottage is quiet now and Ann guesses that Mrs Powe is also at the Rectory sewing, as she does once or twice a week. Mrs Powe would have helped her.

Children in various stages of disarray are spilling out of the next cottage, over the steps and into the road. Ann knows she will not find the medicine she wants here as the Piper family has less money even than her own but she stops as a chorus of small voices calls out to her. Mary-Jane, who is growing tired of being held, struggles to escape and Ann puts her down next to a small girl who is sitting on the steps sharing a crust with a baby on her lap. Two older girls dance around and their young brother, wearing nothing but a long shirt despite the cool breeze, stands and watches with open mouth. Their grown-up sister comes out of the house and stands in the doorway, sewing a glove that she holds in a cloth to keep it clean. Ann feels herself under scrutiny and crouches down to the small children to hide her embarrassment.

"The biy's bad then."

The voice is harsh and Ann is unsure whether an answer is needed. She nods without looking up.

"Us lost three like that."

Ann tightens her grip on the small stick she has been waving to amuse the baby and keeps her eyes on the road. She hears the woman spit on the step then turn back into the cottage, closing the door behind her. Ann thinks again of the medicine. She will ask if it isn't offered. Mary-Jane is sitting on the bottom step and watching, entranced as the children slash at the roadside nettles, so Ann leaves her and walks slowly on to the shop a few doors along.

She opens the door of Gran Hookaway's cottage and walks through the dark passageway into the room on the right, calling out a greeting. Grace Hookaway is sitting by the fire, her back bent so that she stares down at her misshapen, arthritis-ridden hands which lie unmoving in her lap. She twists sideways to look up at Ann and smiles kindly, her weathered, deeply lined face circled by a black woollen scarf under a starched white bonnet.

"How be that little boy then?" She pronounces it "biy" as Ann does herself.

Ann tells her in a rush about how hot he is, the rash that won't go, his quiet otherworldliness this morning and her mother and grandmother's anxious silences. Gran shakes her head and frowns. She can only suggest onion tea and hot flannels and the certainty of recovery when the moon starts to wane. Her reassurances leave Ann feeling even more desperate. The halfpennyworth of tea is scooped from a drawer in the corner where the sacks of flour and sugar, the soap, the bootlaces and other assorted stock is kept. Gran weighs it into a piece of paper then takes a lollipop from a jar in the window and gives to Ann for William. Ann has been given one at a Christmas party once when she was little but William has never had one. Perhaps Gran thinks he should taste one before he dies.

She stands in the road outside the shop. Somehow she must find some ointment for William. She pictures the worried frown disappearing from her mother's face when she hands it over, the quick hug she will be given. She makes her feet move towards the door of the cottage adjoining Gran's and, holding her breath tight inside her, lifts the latch.

The room inside is brighter and more cheerful than most. A gleaming brass kettle hangs above the fire and the blue and white china on the dresser reflects the light from the polished glass of the window. Even the rag rug in front of the hearth is more colourful than the predominantly black rugs found in most cottages. Ann stands rigid in the doorway, unable to call out for fear that her voice will sound high and foolish, when a wordless cry rises from the corner of the room. Ann jumps and clutches at the door. A low bed lies just below the window and a face, open-mouthed, with empty unfocussed eyes raises itself waveringly from the pillow to gaze in Ann's direction. She has seen the girl's face before and it was the knowledge that she would have to see it again that has frightened her as much as having to ask for the medicine. She has seen her twice being cradled by her father outside the cottage and was fascinated and appalled that a girl the same age as herself could be as helpless as the day she was born, and stared as the girl struggled repeatedly to lift her head from her father's shoulder, her mouth ever open in a vacant, dribbling grin. She saw how neighbours teased and patted her as they would a baby, saying,

"Her's a clever maid, her'd talk if her *could* talk, wouldn'ee my chiel," and how the girl wobbled and grinned and crowed and she knew that she would never, ever be able to speak to her like that.

Now the girl cries out again and Ann turns to fly back through the door but a voice calls out from the washhouse at the back,

"What be doing Mary?" and Ann runs instead towards the voice.


Twenty minutes later Ann walks carefully down the hill to Littleham Court with Mary-Jane in one arm and a basket containing the precious pot of Holloway's ointment on the other. The events of the morning race through her mind again; how she had bumped right into Mrs Westcott and burst into tears; how she had hardly been able to say what was wrong for crying until the girl on the mattress began to wail as well and Mrs Westcott had calmed her. Then she had been given a piece of bread with butter and honey on it that was one of the best things she had ever tasted and after that Mrs Westcott had fetched the ointment and wrapped it in a cloth in the basket and had said over and over,

"Now you won't drap'n, will'ee chiel and bring'n back dreckly," and Ann had managed to leave without going any nearer the bed under the window. She hadn't asked for the ointment, she is sure of that, so her mother can't be cross. She had only said that her mother didn't have the money to buy any and that no one they knew had any.

The farmyard is quiet and empty as Ann picks her way through the mud to reach her cottage. She puts Mary-Jane down while she unlatches the door and the little girl clings to her skirt while preparing to launch herself on unsteady legs into the room. As she opens the door Ann becomes aware of voices and recognises a slightly strained civility in her mother's voice. She catches her breath when she sees Mrs Heywood and her eldest daughter Elizabeth, their presence filling the room more surely than her mother's apologetic figure, and for a moment she fears bad news. Once when the chimney caught fire and was threatening to burn the thatch, her mother flew over to the farmhouse and Mrs Heywood had come running out in her long white apron, shouting imperatively to the men. Surely her presence here today must mean bad news. She does not often cross the farmyard to the cottages unless it is to bring a gift of a blanket or a little bonnet when there is a new baby, or to ask Ann's mother to do a day's washing when things are particularly busy at the farmhouse. Ann only visits when taking a message from her mother. She is always a little nervous of knocking on the kitchen door which, as soon as it is opened, reveals a whirlwind of activity directed by the sharp eyes and never-ceasing chatter of Sarah Heywood at its centre. She talks so fast that Ann can only take in half of what she says, which is of no great consequence as her remarks are interspersed with shouted instructions to the servants and sudden dashes to the oven to remove trays of bread or pies. Ann always comes away marvelling at the amount and the variety of food she has seen. If Mrs Heywood is not in the dairy making butter and cream then she is cooking, for five of her seven grown-up children who are still at home. There is her husband William, three servants and Mr Andrew the curate who lodges at Littleham Court, and they all - with the possible exception of Mr Andrew who is rather more dainty in his habits - work hard and have prodigious appetites. With such a busy household to run it is not surprising if Sarah Heywood sounds a little sharp on occasion and if her actions seem governed by long-established habit and a morality implanted during the endless Sunday afternoons in chapel, rather than by any spontaneous empathy. Whatever the source of her actions, she can always be relied on to do the right thing.

Her daughter Elizabeth, 27 and not yet married - though there are rumours of a forthcoming engagement - is slower and more thoughtful in her ways, and it is she who notices Ann now and draws up a chair, speaking quietly under her mother's loud protracted explanations and sudden changes of subject.

"Mother's gwain to send for the doctor to see your little brother. Poor li'l' toad, he bain't very well, be'im? Us heard he was bad and thought us must look in to see 'ee all. But you'm a good girl and help your mother, bain't 'ee?"

Ann nods, her eyes admiring the way Miss Elizabeth's hair is wound expertly around her head. "I got some Holloway's ointment, Mrs Westcott gave it me. He'll flourish now, won't 'im?"

Elizabeth's eyes cloud with doubt and sympathy but Ann does not notice, being distracted for a moment by Mrs Heywood's description of a child at Weare Gifford who had made a dramatic recovery after having brandy and meat ordered by the doctor.

Elizabeth changes the subject. "Us have brought 'ee some cakes. *You'd* like some, wouldn't 'ee, chiel." She swings Mary-Jane, who has remained wide-eyed in the doorway at the shock of seeing the visitors, on to her lap and chatters easily to the two children. Finally her mother makes her farewells, interspersed with graphic descriptions of the many tasks her husband has to perform before he can "saddle up for Bideford" and reassurances that he will nevertheless ride for the doctor that very evening or the next morning at the latest.

Later that afternoon Ann sits on the step with the baby kicking in her lap and her arm around Mary-Jane. Ann stares at the little cake in her hand, admiring the wonderfully yellow honeycomb texture and the fat shiny sultanas, then takes another slow careful bite. Mary-Jane is intent on cramming as much of her cake into her mouth as she can, unaware of the crumbs that fall into her skirt. Ann leans across to pick up a pinch of crumbs and pops them into baby Richard's mouth, which opens like the beak of a fledgling whenever something comes near. He freezes, shocked at the sudden unexpected sweetness and his eyes grow wide and still with surprise. Ann laughs and pokes in more crumbs and this time he makes vigorous sucking movements and coughs at the unfamiliar sensation in his throat. She leans back against the doorframe and gazes into the valley where the road leads down and then onwards towards Bideford. The mist is already beginning to gather in swathes above the twisted course of the stream. She can hear the ringing matched trot of a pair of horses and guesses them to be coming along the carriage drive which leads to Moreton House a mile or so distant. You can stand in the road and look up to see them rattle over Jennett's bridge and sometimes the coachman or one of the occupants glances down, perhaps even Mrs Buck herself. Once when the coach was empty, the coachman grinned and took off his hat to her with a flourish as if she was a lady and she ran back up the road in confusion.

It has been an extraordinary day. John went to school when his jobs were finished - just as well as Mrs. Heywood called - and Ann can hardly wait to tell him of her adventures. She marvels at her daring to go into Mrs. Westcott's cottage, but it was worth it. She has watched as her mother rubbed the pungent ointment into William's chest and throat and has shared in her relief that at last they could do something to help him. Her mother is still checking on him between sweeping the floor, shaking out the rug and peeling the potatoes; the completion of each task marked by her footsteps on the stairs, and as yet he is still sleeping fitfully, his face flushed and damp. But they can rub on some more ointment soon and the doctor is coming, perhaps today if Mr Heywood can find the time to go. She bends down over the baby and presses her mouth against his chest, blowing to make him laugh that sudden formless laugh that bubbles up from deep inside him, then swings him up high up above her head. "He'll flourish, Richie, your big brother's gwain to flourish!"


The room is almost dark. No one has thought to light a candle. Ann leans deep into the fireplace and grasps the handle of the kettle with shaking hands. Rain is falling steadily outside and a drop splashes down the chimney on to her hair, another fizzes in the fire. She braces herself awkwardly to take the weight of the heavy iron kettle and sways back with it on to the hearth. She has put fresh tealeaves in the pot, recklessly throwing the old into the pig bucket. She feels tense and tight inside as if something might burst out of her and she pushes her knees and hands into the hard stone of the hearth. More rain hisses into the fire. It is the only sound. She wants to say something, shout to break the silence. She remembers her father throwing a sack over his shoulders and stumbling out into the late wet afternoon. Was it only a few minutes ago? He muttered something about going to Bideford, got to report it, he said. Pictures flash before her. The doctor standing still and silent as if listening while he holds William's wrist. William's eyes opening, unseeing, slowly closing again. A whimper. The doctor's hands, smoother than her father's, that move knowingly over William's body, pausing here and there as if they can see right inside. The quiet voices and then the long hours of waiting. Her mother's sudden cry.

Ann rises woodenly with the cup of black tea and carries it to the table where her mother sits motionless with John and Mary-Jane. Even Mary-Jane sits silent, frightened. As Ann puts the cup down her mother turns to her and their eyes meet. There are dark hollows under the gaunt cheekbones; her eyes are wide, dark and startled. Ann feels as if the breath has been knocked out of her and she flings her arms around her mother as the tension gushes out of her in big stuttering sobs. They cling to each other, reaching out to include John and Mary-Jane and between the sobs comes Ann's voice, tremulous but resolute,

"I'll look after 'ee Mother, I will, I'll look after 'ee."

# CHAPTER ONE

The registers of baptisms and burials for Littleham were brought to me on a wet and windy night in October, heavy foolscap tomes bearing evidence of their age in the foxed covers and worn binding, now barely holding the pages in place. I opened the burials register first and turned the pages carefully until I found those with the words 'Burials in the Parish of Littleham in the County of Devon in the Year 1871' inscribed carefully at the top. There were three pages. The names I knew from the churchyard stones drew my attention at once and it seemed to me that there was sadness even in the ancient faded ink in which they were written. There were other names too, perhaps of those too poor to have their graves marked. I turned to the Baptisms Register and found many of the same names but this time with more information, the names and occupation of the parents and the place of abode, sometimes just given as Littleham but sometimes a particular farm or row of cottages. I moved from one register to the other, cross-referencing and making notes until I began to build up a nebulous outline of the families I was beginning to feel close to. I trawled further back to find parents and grandparents in the earliest entries at the beginning of the century then counted names and dates. The average number of deaths in Littleham from 1813 - the first entry - to 1899 was just under six each year. In 1871 there were 21 deaths. 13 of those were children under 12 years old.

Eventually, finding it hard to focus on the sad testimony, I found that the hours had passed more quickly than I had realised; it was now three o'clock in the morning. I called to my dog and went out into the dark, silent village for a last walk. The rain had stopped and a half moon made a fleeting appearance until clouds racing against a stormy sky again hid it from view. I stood still and looked around me. In the near darkness no power lines or television aerials were visible, no modern fences or double-glazed windows, but only the faint silhouettes of wind-blown trees and unlit cottages. The centuries seemed to coalesce; times past and those yet to come with all their attendant loves, losses, joys and sorrows became one.

After returning the Burials and Baptisms Registers to the church, I took stock of the information I now possessed. In a notebook I had listed, on separate pages, the names and ages of all those who were buried in Littleham churchyard in 1871, the dates on which they were buried and the rector or curate who officiated. Below each name I had copied references to that surname from the registers in an attempt to trace the correct family. This had not always been easy as in some cases the surnames occurred very frequently. It was time to search for other sources of information.

The first full census took place in 1841, listing the names of people in each household, their ages, occupations and county of birth. There has been a census every ten years since then incorporating greater detail and the records are an invaluable aid to genealogical and historical research. It was fortunate for me that a census took place on April $2^{nd}$ 1871, the very year in which I was interested.

Once a week for the next few weeks I drove the twelve miles to the Record Office and Local Studies Library in Barnstaple, leaving Littleham early and only returning when the office was due to close. On each occasion I parked my car and walked over the ancient long bridge alongside others intent on their own separate purposes. Then along the narrow shopping street thronged with people and as I drew nearer, my pace increased with the anticipation of leaving the noisy, brash, twenty-first century behind and stepping into another, quieter era.

Barnstaple Library is housed in a modern brick building next to the old cattle market, a strange juxtaposition on market days when the lowing of cattle could until recently be heard amidst the traffic noise, providing a reminder of the days when Barnstaple was first and foremost an agricultural centre. This contrast between the ultramodern and the ancient was particularly apparent to me on these days when, although surrounded by all the trappings of modern life, it was the past that was calling out to me. I walked up the stairs past the main library to the Local Studies Library and Record Office, a quiet room redolent with the scent of old books and the hum of modern machinery. Having asked for the 1871 Census for Littleham, I settled myself in front of a film reader, a device which makes it possible to read the microfilm copies of the census and other documents.

There were usually several other people working in the room, either consulting books, original documents and maps at the large oak tables or leaning towards the screens of microfiche and film readers, intent on deciphering the antique script. The atmosphere was always one of intense concentration for this is not a place where one tends to while away a few idle hours, nor a place where one is told to go and work; all those who visit tend to be driven by a fierce desire to discover the truth about certain distant lives and events, a compulsion which can threaten to overtake the more immediate concerns of the present.

Moving quietly so as not to disturb those already at work, I organised my notebooks and pen on the desk and carefully drew up the chair. Having switched on the machine so that its hum tuned in with those already operating, I pushed the reel of film on to the drive wheel and turned the dial to send images spinning across the large screen. Invariably a moment's incomprehension would be followed by the realisation that the picture was upside down and out of focus and further adjustments were necessary before the jumble of runes and hieroglyphics resolved themselves into English. It was then a matter of holding the dial on fast forward to run through the census returns for other local villages, turning my head away all the while as the speed of the words flying across the screen had the same effect on my stomach as a particularly tempestuous fairground ride, until I reached the returns for Littleham.

It occurred to me for the first time that I would not find the names of many of the deceased in this census as most of the deaths had taken place before April 2nd. However, in many cases I knew the names of their parents and was soon able to find the family listed in the census. When I did not have these details and the surname was one that was common in the village, the only way I could guess from which family they had originated was to notice ominous gaps between the ages of the children in the family. In many families at that time a new baby was born every two years, so a four-year gap between children very often indicated a death. In this way it was not long before I was able to find all the details I wanted. When I could picture the houses in which the parents lived, knew their names, ages and occupations, the names and ages of their other children, then their faces too seemed to come into focus and I felt I shared in their grief and in the solace they found in their remaining children. The lost children had seemed destined to be forgotten as moss gradually filled in the letters carved into the gravestones, ivy obscured the moss and finally the stones cracked and fell. Perhaps it would not have mattered, more than a hundred years later, if they were no longer remembered. As individuals they have, as far as we know, no exceptional significance but the story of their fate and their family's grief, how their family lived and spent their days, is the story of thousands of other families in villages throughout Britain, during the nineteenth century and beyond. They are our past, and they inform our present.

While reading through the census, the many facts it contained constantly distracted me from my desire to find the families of those who had died. I marvelled at the size of the families - six or eight children was common; the frequent repetition of surnames and of Christian names - so many called Mary, Mary Anne, William, John; the now unfamiliar occupations such as gloveress and brewery labourer and the multitude of farm labourers. I studied the place names, matching the dwellings with my knowledge of the village today, and pictured the hedges and fields where modern houses now stood.

Littleham is a village of almost 400 inhabitants three miles from the market town of Bideford in north Devon and two miles from the nearest main road. The village sits amongst wooded and pasture slopes with glimpses down to the valley of the tree-lined River Yeo and over to the high ridges and skyline church towers of Monkleigh, Buckland Brewer and Parkham villages. Like many small Devon villages Littleham sits at the centre of a web of narrow sunken lanes which wind between high banks; visitors are frequently confused by the choice of routes, each of which brings them to a different part of the scattered village. The pub and the village hall are at opposite ends of the village, and the church is at the end of a lane a quarter of a mile from other houses. There is no longer a school or a shop or a post office and the pub attracts more people from Bideford, three miles away, who come to eat in the restaurant than it does locals. The church still attracts a small but loyal congregation as does the chapel, and skittle and bingo nights at the village hall are well supported albeit by as many from outside the village as within it. Like most villages today, Littleham is inhabited mainly by people who enjoy a rural view from their windows but who rely on nearby towns for their employment, their shopping and their social lives.

It was clear from the census that the Littleham of 1871 was a very different place. Being three miles from Bideford it was obvious that before motorised transport the village must have been a much more self-sufficient community and this was borne out by the details in the census. Unlike the mainly professional occupations of today, in 1871 a large proportion of the 394 inhabitants were involved in farming and others such as blacksmiths, butchers and millers depended on farmers to make a living. Other occupations were also carried out in the village making visits to neighbouring towns unnecessary; there were glovers working from home, shopkeepers, carpenters, shoemakers, joiners, masons, brewery labourers and dressmakers. The columns in the census headed "Where Born" were also informative. Whereas today a small minority of the inhabitants are born in Devon and only a handful in the village itself, in 1871 almost half were born in the village and most of the remainder came from surrounding villages such as Monkleigh, Buckland Brewer and Abbotsham. Of those who were born in the village, the same surnames appeared again and again: Dennis, Westcott, Piper, Morrish, Hockin. I was beginning to build up a picture of a community where one knew all one's neighbours, was related to many of them and had little need to leave the village either for employment or basic commodities. Trips to Bideford were probably necessary for items such as new clothes and household goods, but a glance through the nature of the jobs listed under "Rank, Profession or Occupation" and the large number of children in each family indicated that money would rarely be available for such luxuries, that survival was probably enough of an achievement.

I walked around Littleham with transcribed notes from the 1871 census in my hand, trying to match the older houses with the written record. Some house bore names that were relatively unchanged, but many were unnamed in the census and there frequently seemed to be too many houses listed in a given location. There were six houses listed at Moorhead, but a walk down this hill on the outskirts of the village revealed only four pristine modernised houses, which could however have been divided to provide six dwellings for the labourers, gardeners and shoemakers who lived there in 1871. Similarly I could imagine the eight dwellings listed as Langdon Cottages and Lower Langdon Cottages when I looked at the houses, no longer subdivided, known as Middle, Gregory's and Little Langdon, and the three modern houses with double garages which had been built on the site of an old ruin. I remembered when that site had been a haven for foxes and when butterflies had danced over the brambles that hid the tumbledown walls; now I could picture the butcher and farmer who had lived and worked there with their families. I imagined the astonishment they would feel if they could see the houses that stand there today.

I was not experienced in historical research and no doubt went about things in a disorganised fashion, so it was a while before it occurred to me that an old map would be useful. Once again the local studies library proved invaluable. I was shown two maps, one drawn from the tithe map of 1841 and showing all the field names in use at that time, and the other dated 1889. As I pored over them, it soon became clear that I would need more than one day to study all the details and I was able to have photocopies made to take home with me. I then spent many hours with the sheets of paper laid out on the floor like a jigsaw puzzle, comparing one with the other, and both of them with my knowledge of the village of 1871 and of today, and of twenty years previously when I had first moved to Littleham. As I studied the maps I saw not black lines but hedges resplendent with primroses and the call of chaffinches, not small grey rectangles but houses I knew, sometimes with a face at the window and smoke from the chimney. An hour or two's scrutiny was as good as a long walk during which one travelled through time as well as space; down half-familiar lanes where today's towering oaks were young saplings; past the immaculate, right-angled barn conversion that changed before my eyes into the tumbledown, bramble-grown hovel of 20 years ago then again to the nineteenth century thatched cob barn, full of sheaves of corn. Finally I would look up, surprised to find myself still on the floor of the study and the year unchanged.

While working in the Record Office I discovered by chance that the census of 1851 had been published on CD by the Church of Jesus Christ of Latter-day Saints as an aid to researching family history. This only covered three counties but it happened that one of them was Devon. Once I had obtained a copy I was able to greatly extend my knowledge of the families in which I was interested by tracing them back in time using these search facilities. Later the 1881 census also became available. By typing in the first name, year and place of birth of an individual, I was able to find her in the 1851 census and discover her maiden name, dwelling and details of her parents. I arranged to have photocopies of the 1861 and 1871 census for Littleham and was then able to trace families over a period of 30 years from the comfort of my home.

By now I had a much clearer picture of the village of 1871 and knew at least a little about the families of those who appeared in the Burials Register for that year. I did not yet know what had caused so many deaths in such a short time.

# *Wednesday 14th December 1870.*

Lucy Glover leaves her cottage at East Furlong and turns up the lane, pausing outside the old farmhouse to count as the clock strikes inside. The sounds and sights of the village have attended her early morning chores, an accompaniment of which she is barely aware but which reassures her that all is progressing as it should. She has been woken by the first cockerel shouting a reminder that the day has begun; it has been answered by another, and another, then cows low and a dog barks. Blue wood smoke has been rising for more than an hour from the chimneys of Boundstone and East Furlong Farms by the time she blows out the candle in her front window. She looks out to see that the glow of candles has been extinguished from other cottage windows in response to the lightening sky and the illumination from newly lit fires. From further up the hill a door has slammed, followed by the quick ring of steel on stone as the man of the house hurries down the steps in his nailed boots. Later the first children have appeared, girls and toddlers in shawls wrapped and knotted at the back, boys in cut down jackets, to sit on the step and eat a cold potato or a hunk of bread without dropping crumbs on a newly swept floor.

The clock finishes its striking. Eight o'clock. This is the time her husband William starts work in the cobbler's shop in Bideford, people being more particular about clock time in towns, and she worries about him being late although she knows he walks fast and is good at judging the sun's height. He earns more money in Bideford than he would be able to in the village, there being three shoemakers here already and little enough to spend on new boots. Here in Littleham boots are reheeled and patched and resoled until there is little left of the original materials. Lucy and William have talked and schemed in the evenings when the babies are settled and the fire dying down and, though their plans are interspersed with many ifs and if onlys, they think they might one day be able to rent a little house in Bideford.

Today she has an extra reason for listening to the clock for she has somewhere to go herself and, although no specific time has been mentioned, there are chores she has to finish before she sets off on her mission. She feels a thrill of uncertainty and excitement as she thinks of it. First, there is water to fetch. She has left the baby in her wooden cradle near the fire and three year old Harriet sitting at the table eating a slice of bread and dripping. It is good to be out in the light after yesterday's rain and an entire day passed in the oppressive darkness of the cottage. She can smell the milkiness of the cattle and hear the clang of buckets; from Mount Pleasant a questioning voice, a reply and answering laugh. Lucy smiles with anticipation. She has to pass the cottages to reach the well and there is always someone with news to tell or an amusing tale to share.

The first cottage is set high above the lane with steep steps leading up to the front door. Maria Westcott is standing at the bottom, arms folded over the clean white apron she always wears, talking to Martha Powe who is on her knees scrubbing the top step. "Mornin'." Lucy stops as she greets them but does not put down her buckets. Do they know where she is going today? Should she tell them? She is aware that they are both looking quizzically at her and she falters, not knowing what to say next, until Mrs Westcott speaks for her.

"You'm off down Knowle then, maid."

She nods mutely. Martha Powe sits back on her heels and pushes her hair from her eyes.

"Don' 'ee worry about it, maid, you'll be all right and you'll be 'elpin' out Mrs Prouse." She changes the subject. "'Ave 'ee yurd 'ee be gwain off again, Rector?" Martha's husband is groom and butler at the Rectory so passes on all the news to the village.

"He be gwain up to Lunnon for to see to *business* but what

he dos there I don't know." She takes up her scrubbing brush again and splashes it in the bucket of water. "But us'll be seeing yet more of Mr Andrew and that'll please some folks I know." Lucy joins in the laughter and goes on her way.

She leaves the houses behind and continues down the narrow high-hedged lane towards the well. Ahead she can see two bowed figures with a bucket between them and recognises Gran Hookaway with her friend and lodger Miss Sarah Brooks. She hurries on to reach the well as they do and puts her own buckets down.

"Here, Gran, I'll fill it for 'ee", and she lets down the bucket almost before the two old women have realised she is there.

"That's kind of 'ee my bird, us *can* do it but 'tis a struggle 'cos us don't bend quite as well as us did. Now you should be careful too, 'tis only a few weeks since you brought forth that chiel, don't go over reaching yourself."

"I'm strong again now Gran, 'twas much easier this time."

Lucy leaves her own buckets by the well and carries the water back for the two old women, walking slowly to keep pace with them as they hobble along arm in arm. Gran tells her how weak she'd been for months after her first child and how hard it had been managing in an old place with rain streaming down the cracked walls from a rotting and shapeless thatched roof and the fire always smoking.

"That old house has gone now, thank the Lord. Littleham was a wild old place to live then, quite different from the tidy place it is now. The roads was so muxy you couldn't get to town and some folks never left here all their lives. Us had bats in the bedroom and rats in the larder. You'd have been afeared if you'd lived then!"

Lucy exclaims at the description, which she has heard many times before. They reach the tiny two-roomed cottage where the two women sleep, eat and keep shop, apparently without ever exchanging a cross word, perhaps because Gran does the talking for them both. She pats Lucy's arm now and looks up into her face, her small, birdlike eyes shining out from her lined, weathered features.

"'Tis always a pleasure to see 'ee Lucy, you'm always so pretty and smiling and full of life it sets me up for the day." Miss Brooks nods in agreement though it is not really clear whether she is listening as her broad, placid features rarely show any emotion.

Lucy says goodbye and turns away in confusion, walking back down the hill to the well. Is it true what Gran has said? She knows William thinks her very pretty especially when she takes off her night-gown - she smiles at the memory - but it has never occurred to her that other people might share his opinion. Can it be that Mrs Prouse thinks her lively and attractive? Is that why she has asked her to visit today? After all there are other women in the village with young babies.

When she reaches her cottage she puts down the two buckets with relief, letting fall the child's hoop that she wears around her waist to prevent the buckets banging against her legs. Her cottage is one of three belonging to East Furlong Farm and no longer needed for farm workers, though it is in any case doubtful whether any but the most desperate worker would agree to live in any of them. The thatch is thin and grey, the cob walls patched and uneven, the window frames crumbling and the whole seeming to sink back down into the earth from whence they came. William has patched up their house as best he can and it is at least warm and dry inside. Their neighbours, both widows with young children, fare less well though admittedly better than Gran Hookaway had done. Lucy shivers. She knows what it is to be uncertain of the future, to be less than respectable and she does not intend to let it happen again.

When Lucy was a child she saw very little of her mother, who was a shadowy, apologetic figure who visited the farm on a Sunday when her work allowed, sometimes bringing a ribbon for Lucy or a penny for Henry. Her father never showed any great pleasure at seeing her despite most of the visit being spent upstairs, and Lucy suspects now that the woman who had borne him two children had become an embarrassment to him, along with the presence in the farm cottage of his estranged wife and her son whose parentage had never, to Lucy's knowledge, been established. Certainly he took the opportunity, once he was free to remarry, of starting afresh and marrying from out of the area and seems happier now with Fanny than she has ever known him. He has always been kind to Lucy in a remote way but it was her brother Henry that she depended on for love and advice throughout her childhood. Isolated as they were at Lower Dunn, they presented a united front when obliged to go to the village or when confronted with awkward questions at school. Henry always answered for her when the inevitable question arose. "What *is* your name now, is it Dennis or is it Clark like your father?" All that is over now. She escaped by marrying William, and her brother Henry by going to London. She misses him terribly.

She opens the door. "Well, Harriet Ann Glover and Selena Elizabeth Glover, what be'ee to?"

"I rockin' baby to sleep" replies Harriet, redoubling her efforts rather too energetically, while Selena sleeps on, unaware of the violent motions of the cradle which threaten to throw her out.

"Well, I be setting out to feed her now so leave her be and go and play. After that you'm both gwain to Mrs Vilot's for a bit while I go out."

The decision as to whether to feed the baby before going out has been a hard one. If she gives her a full feed she might have none left for the other baby whose well being is the purpose of her journey. If she does not feed her she might wake and cry and Lucy is afraid that Ann Vilot might give her some laudanum to keep her quiet. She used to give it to her own children every day so she could get on with her gloving. Most people say it is wonderful how it can make children sleep, but Lucy has noticed how many babies belonging to single mothers who have to glove to support themselves die young, often without apparent cause. She knows that some people say it is the laudanum that sends them away and she has always turned down the offer of it by well-meaning neighbours for her own babies. The solution, she has decided, is to give Selena a small feed before she is really hungry. She lifts the sleeping baby from the cradle and settles down in the chair by the fire.

An hour later as Lucy leaves Ann Vilot's cottage the early morning sounds have settled into the rhythms of the day. The promise of sunshine has died as the sun rose behind a shroud of thin white cloud that arches up and around to meet the earth again. There is the faintest stirring breeze, just enough to rasp the last withered leaves in the roadside hedge and cause a cat picking her way immaculately through the long grass to look sharply up. It is mild for December. In the farmyards the morning rounds are done and the day's work underway. In Float Meadow behind Boundstone a shout goes up and a shiny bay horse steps ponderously onward, its massive shoulders thrown forward to plough the first straight furrow. From the blacksmith's shop at Langdon the sound of iron striking metal rings out in a steady beat across the fields, each new onslaught sounding before the reverberation of the last has ceased and forming a continuous clangour which rouses a flock of jackdaws from the hedgerow elms and sends them whirling and exclaiming into the sky.

She leaves the school and the last house behind and walks up the hill out of the village. She has kept on her long, white apron to protect her cotton print dress and has added a wing bonnet and brightly coloured plaid shawl fastened at the neck. She smiles as she remembers Harriet and four year old Charles staring wide-eyed at each other as if they had never seen each other before. She knows they will soon be playing out in the lane together as they do most days, though she doesn't turn Harriet out in all weathers as Ann Vilot does Charles. She loves the serious, knowing little comments Harriet makes as she helps her with the chores and likes to keep the child with her at least some of the day.

Her thoughts jump ahead to her forthcoming meeting and her stomach tightens with nervous anticipation. She has not been to Knowle Farm since she used to visit occasionally with her father to sell some surplus hay or ask for extra help for harvest. The farm is run by Ann Prouse and her son Thomas, though he was still young in the days when Lucy used to visit. She does some sums in her head, counting back over the years and then forward again. He must be about 19 now and Sarah would be the same for they are twins, the only ones Lucy has ever known. It is because of Sarah that she is going there today. Lucy has never known her well, for she is three years younger and rarely came up to school as a child, but her husband James Middleton is an old childhood friend. Lucy can remember him racing hoops with Henry along the frost-hardened track to Lower Dunn, both boys with their eyes fixed on their hoops as they darted alongside them, beating and urging them on as if they were horses. Sarah has had a fever for over a week now and her milk has dried up but Mrs Prouse has said she will be all right in another week or so. Lucy tries to picture herself with two babies - three, for Harriet still likes to be cuddled and held. What will she do when they all cry?

She draws her shawl around her as she passes the three-cornered field, known as Tweenaway as it is positioned like an island between three lanes with a choice of direction at each corner, and turns down the more exposed north-facing hill. The road here is drier and less rutted, for Mr Heywood at Littleham Court sees that the stone breakers regularly throw down new stones, and she is able to let go of her skirt and lengthen her stride. The landscape is laid out before her, a patchwork of green pasture and brown plough interspersed with the russets and duns of hedgerow and woodland spreading as far as she can see. She breathes deeply as she walks, smiling a little as she raises her head to let the breeze caress her face, and thinks how good it is to be alone for a while. Ahead she sees a small figure leave one of the cottages at Littleham Court and lurch across the road with a large burden. As she gets nearer she sees it is a young girl with a large basket of washing under one arm and holding a child, little more than a baby, by the hand. After a few more steps she sees it is Ann Williams, whose brother died of fever a few weeks ago. Lucy went to the funeral along with all of those in the village who could get away from work for an hour and cried when she saw the tiny coffin. Mrs Williams looked to be beyond tears, her face thin and haunted and Lucy saw how Ann held on to her mother as if she was the one doing the caring, although she was only 12 years old.

By the time Lucy reaches Ann she is standing up on the verge spreading the washing out on the hedge to dry, with the baby clinging on to her leg for balance. The quick confidence of her movements seem strange in a young girl and it occurs to Lucy that this is not a task she is carrying out at her mother's request but one for which she is totally responsible. Nevertheless she calls out,

"Helpin' your mother then Ann?"

"Oh yes, I be carin' for her now. I bain't gwain to school no more, there be too much to do. Don't it take a lot of blue to get the aprons white?"

Lucy stops and looks at the clothes that Ann is throwing up on to the hedge. The hawthorn and bramble catch at them and hold them in place and the cloth is too coarse to be easily torn, though some have been darned and mended many times.

"You must catch rainwater if the well water's brown, us has to up in the village. How is your mother?"

Ann straightens up and frowns, pushing back a strand of hair that has escaped to fall across her face. She is wearing her hair up now, which, together with the cut-down dress of her mother's she is wearing, makes her look far older than her age.

"Her's not too viddy. Her's got an awful cough and no more strength nor a kitten. But her'll be all right 'cos I can do the work now, see. Her says her depends on me now."

Ann picks up Mary Jane and settles the child on her hip which she pushes out sideways to accommodate her, her slim child's body being as yet unequipped for the purpose.

"I've no time to stay talking now, I've glovin' to do," and

she struts back to the cottage from which Lucy can hear a baby crying. She watches her go and the set of the girl's back is so independent that she swallows an impulse to call after her to take care, to ask for help, we'd all be happy to help.

The lane continues on down the hill, winding a little between the high hedge banks which shut out the view across the fields to either side like blinkers on a carrier's horse, focussing Lucy's mind on the task ahead. She is shy of meeting anyone on the track to the farm or in the yard. Who works there now? What will she say if they ask her business? All too soon she reaches the place where the farm track leads off to the left, just above where Jennett's bridge crosses the road and she feels the knot in her stomach tighten. The track winds and dips between overhanging trees then divides by the confluence of two streams, one path leading on to a footbridge and the other fording the stream and continuing up the hill to run alongside the carriage drive to the great house at Moreton. She stands on the footbridge and leans on the handrail listening to the water that rushes beneath and around her, almost drowning the song of a robin perched on the lowest branch of an oak. The track is edged with bracken, the fronds now deep russet and yellow, and on the slopes above she can see the glossy green of the rhododendrons that line the carriage drive. She lifts her skirts up out of the mud and continues along the track to Knowle, remembering other times she has come this way. Once when she was very young, up in the horse-drawn trap squeezed between her father and Henry, they had called in to see Mrs Prouse on their way to market. She and Henry had waited in the trap while their father went into the house and she remembered how close they had sat with a sack over their knees for warmth. The cows in the yard had jostled against the trap making it rock and she had been relieved to see the door open and her father emerge shouting farewells which echoed through the cold still air. Another time - she would have been 11 or 12 - she walked with him on a warm summer's evening just before harvest. He held her hand in a vicelike yet comforting grip and she had closed her eyes as they walked to shut out the glare from the setting sun, letting herself be led along. They did not speak a word to each other all the way there and all the way back but in the farmhouse there was laughter and joviality as they sat at the long kitchen table eating the slices of potato pasty that Mrs Prouse passed around. In her memory some details are sharp and clearly defined like objects next to a lighted candle while others are as shadowy as the darkest corner of a room. At the moment Ann Prouse's face is barely discernible to her although it is only a few months since they last met and she feels she will be more at ease when her features come into the light.

At last the farmhouse comes into view and as Lucy unhooks the five-barred gate which straddles the narrow entrance leading into the yard she is relieved to see just a few cattle standing disconsolately in the mud and a smooth-coated black and white collie who bounds towards her barking and scattering hens, before circling around behind her to sniff at her ankles. She is picking her way through the mud when there is a rattle of buckets from the cowshed to her right and the door flies open, making her jump. Ann Prouse is wearing an old-fashioned poke bonnet that emphasises the moonlike roundness of her face, the strings flying loose each side of her voluminous chin. She breaks into a wide grin, displacing enough flesh to make her eyes almost disappear.

"Hello my bird, all right then? 'Tis good of you to come and help us out like this, I've been as anxious as a hen over that little chiel. Come on in now and have a dish of tay."

She waddles across the yard wiping her hands on her rough hessian apron and Lucy follows her, beginning to relax.

As Mrs Prouse opens the kitchen door they hear a weak crying and she hurries in, clucking and cooing, while Lucy hovers in the doorway. The housemaid, a young girl of 12 or 13 who is introduced as Priscilla, is walking to and fro in front of the fireplace jiggling a young baby against her shoulder. Mrs Prouse takes her granddaughter and rocks and croons her into acquiescence.

"Her's taken a little milk this morning but 'twas hardly sufficient to keep a fly from thirst." She gazes earnestly at Lucy. "I'll be so thankful if her takes to you. Now I'll make the tea so sit yourself down. Will you take her now?"

Lucy sits down on the high settle by the fire and apprehensively takes the baby being proffered to her. The first thing she notices is her weight: although clearly underfed, the baby is nearly two months older than Selena and feels lumpish by comparison. She gazes down at the unfamiliar little face among the shawls which stares back at her for a moment then crumples and cries again.

"Ellen, Ellen, come on then, come on."

She moves the baby against her shoulder, aware again of the clumsy size of the child and the unfamiliar smell now that she is close. She talks and rocks but already feels that she is failing. It is clear that Ellen does not like her. Ann Prouse turns to her.

"Try her now if you want, my bird. Her's hungry for sure. Priscilla, go and do the bedrooms and see if Sarah wants for anything."

For Priscilla is standing open-mouthed, her eyes examining Lucy from head to toe. Lucy unbuttons her dress with one hand and moves Ellen back into the crook of her arm and towards her bare breast. Suddenly the baby stops crying and with a fierce greedy look in her eye seizes the nipple, only to wrench her head away almost immediately and resume crying with redoubled effort and volume.

"There, there, 'tis all right, come on." Mrs Prouse sits down beside Lucy and takes the baby from her. "You don't smell like her mother you see, 'tis just the same with lambs but her'll come round, - you must do, my chiel, mustn't you?"

Lucy covers herself and sits sipping her tea, feeling tense and uncomfortable despite Mrs Prouse's reassurances. She would like to walk out of the kitchen and back down the track then and there, to be back in her own cottage with her own babies and not think of this again. But what if Ellen should die?

"Try again now my bird, her's calmer again now."

She takes the baby again and the performance is repeated but this time Ellen reaches for the nipple a second time and takes a few desperate sucks before breaking away again yelling and spluttering. Lucy coaxes her, touching her cheek with her finger and after a few more false starts the baby is greedily sucking and swallowing and Lucy feels the tension gradually melt away both from her body and from the little child in her lap. Eventually the sucking slows and each swallow is followed by a little satisfied exhalation and a small hand wavers upwards and blindly, unconsciously, caresses Lucy's neck.

Now that the problem is resolved Ann Prouse goes upstairs to tell her daughter the good news. Lucy moves Ellen on to her shoulder and as the baby drowses and hiccups, she drinks her tea and takes in her surroundings for the first time. Compared to her own home they are opulent; the room is large and well-furnished with two large settles by the fire; a glass-fronted dresser containing decorated plates and cups, jugs of all sizes and two large teapots; a trunk on which stands a small barrel of cider and a broad platter; and the table is, large enough for 12 or 15 people and indeed surrounded by forms and chairs sufficient to seat that number. The massive fireplace is hung with plentiful cooking pots and everywhere Lucy looks there is food available to cook; sides of fat bacon hang from the ceiling; on the table is a wooden half-barrel of apples, a flour hutch and a quantity of pastry in the process of being rolled and through a small door she can catch a glimpse of the pantry shelves lined with jars of jam, pickle and honey and a large pie on a plate. There are pictures on the kitchen walls and on the mantelpiece above the clavel beam is a wooden salt box, a tinderbox and a china dog that Lucy particularly admires.

The door to the stairs opens again and Priscilla appears with a tray, closely followed by Ann Prouse.

"Well, 'tis all fixed my bird, Sarah's agreeable for you to take her though it breaks her heart that she can't care for the chiel herself of course. Poor lamb. Her'd like you to come up and see her and say goodbye to the chiel. Will you come?"

Lucy follows her up the narrow creaking staircase and they pass first through what she takes to be Mrs Prouse's chamber, although she is too confused by the unfamiliarity of the day's experiences to take in more than a fleeting impression, then through a latch door to James and Sarah's chamber. Sarah is cocooned in the deep feather bed, her hair drawn dark and flat around her pallid face and her heavy-lidded eyes dull and unhappy. Mrs Prouse does the talking and Lucy barely hears what she says, for she feels uncomfortable holding the child that should by rights be with its mother. At last she realises Mrs Prouse is encouraging them to say their farewells and she holds Ellen out and Sarah reaches out a trembling hand and touches the child's cheek. For the first time she meets Lucy's gaze and whispers a "thank you" as her eyes fill with tears.

"I'll look after her like my own," Lucy promises and as they troop back down the stairs, she finds she is crying too.

At the door Mrs Prouse is brisk and matter-of-fact, keeping emotion at arm's length. Lucy is to walk home with Ellen now and after dinner Mrs Prouse will come up to the village with the pony and trap and bring more shawls and wrappings, the wooden cradle and some food and milk.

"You'll need plenty of vittles, my bird, if you'm sucklin' two." She will bring a side of bacon, a freshly baked apple pie, half a gallon of milk and a piece of cheese. Would Lucy like some jam too? James will be so grateful when he gets back from work and it will only be for a week or two, until Sarah is strong again. Before she knows what is happening, Lucy finds herself walking back down the lane with the baby in her arms, taking deep draughts of fresh air to compensate for the suffocating sensation of being enveloped and hugged by Ann Prouse.

In the fireplace the Yule log spits, crackles and flares, briefly lighting up the room that will soon be in need of a candle. Lucy looks across at her husband dozing in the Windsor chair, his long legs thrust out in front of him and crossed at the ankle, the fire gleaming on the shine of his boots, highly polished before chapel that morning. His arms are folded across his black Sunday waistcoat, his chin slumped on his chest. She smiles at his sideburns, which she is sure grow a little longer each week. She has teased him that they will soon meet under his chin like his father's. She is barely awake herself. It has been the best Christmas she can remember. She is certain she has never eaten so much in her life before. Again relief floods through her that the goose was cooked just right, the skin crisp and not too burnt, the flesh rich and tender, the juices running clear. She had never cooked one before and took advice from anyone who would offer it.

For a while yesterday it had seemed that Christmas would be a frugal affair indeed, for the delicacies that Ann Prouse had promised for the occasion could not be brought on the pony. There was a severe frost that had lasted for four days, not even loosening its grip during the daylight hours as the sun failed to penetrate the leaden skies. Each morning she had to break the ice on the water jug in her bedroom before she could wash and at night she placed the cradles close to the chimneybreast in her bedroom in the hope that the babies would gain some warmth from the fire which smouldered in the room below. It had been several days since she had heard the sound of horses' hooves on the road outside and as the hours had passed yesterday with no sign of a thaw she had wished she had asked William to visit the Christmas market to buy a duck or even a piece of pork for their dinner. Finally there was a shout and a knock on the door and there was Sarah's husband James and his young nephew William laden with baskets and packages, having slithered and skated up from Knowle. After they had taken tea and James cuddled his baby daughter and she had bid them farewell and Merry

Christmas, she had opened the parcels and gazed in amazement. Besides the goose there was brawn, a meat pie, milk, cheese, pickle, apples, nuts and, best of all, a Christmas pudding.

Now as she drowses in front of the fire with the babies asleep in their cradles at her feet and Harriet chattering to herself as she plays some elaborate game under the table, she thinks of the little pot of money on the mantel shelf and how it has increased in the past week as she has had to buy so little. Then as the huge ashen faggot spits again she thinks of the brand that they will put away tonight and bring out for next year's fire to show that the cycle of life goes on. She cannot picture the coming year and what it will bring but, as she closes her eyes, the fires of all the Christmases to come stretch out before her in an endless procession, and she falls asleep.

Five days later Lucy is in the little yard behind her cottage, struggling to turn the handle on the mangle with one hand while holding Ellen on her hip with the other. She has managed to feed Selena and get her to sleep between washing yet more piles of the babies' cloths, but now Ellen is hungry and Lucy wants to hang out the washing before she sits down again. She is tired after having to get up twice in the night for Ellen who is teething, and her arms ache after a morning spent carrying buckets of water and pummelling and wringing the washing. Harriet is trying to help by holding up the next cloth from the bucket and calling out "'Nother one, mama, 'nother one," while dripping water on Lucy's feet and she clenches her teeth to stop herself snapping at the child and destroying the hopeful enthusiasm in the little upturned face. Suddenly she hears a loud knocking on the front door and a voice calling

"Lucy! Lucy!"

She hurries round the side of the cottage and almost bumps

into Mrs Powe coming round to meet her. She knows straightaway that something is wrong. Martha Powe is looking pale and shocked and stands silent for a moment, looking from Lucy to the baby in her arms, then her eyes fill with tears.

"The poor little chiel," she says, reaching out a hand to Ellen, "'Tis Sarah, her's passed away."

Martha and Lucy are sitting at the table with cups of tea. Lucy is feeding Ellen and Martha holds Selena in her lap but neither of the women pays any attention to the babies. The room is silent but for the little sighs Ellen makes every time she swallows. Lucy feels drained and weary after the crying which followed her initial shock. She reaches for her tea and looks over at Martha, who has rushed out without putting on her bonnet and looks pale in her dark high-necked dress and hair pulled severely back. Their eyes meet.

"'Tisn't over yet you know," says Martha. "I hear little Sarah Dennis over at Langdon is very bad with the fever. The Shutte children down at Edge Mill Cottages have it and the two youngest Pipers alongside of me. They'm thirsty all the time and want to do nothing but lie about."

Lucy stares at her wide-eyed.

"Sarah's that bad? And the *Pipers*? Mrs Powe, you didn't tell me! Is it the fever?"

Martha nods. "But don't take on so, they all has to have it sometime. Though 'tis true it seems bad this time. 'Tisn't often it takes people away once they'm grown and I know a lot died in Appledore and Northam before Christmas. But mine, they'm strong. Though I don't know about Sarah Dennis, they've had the doctor out and that's always a bad sign."

She sighs. "And you? What be gwain to do 'bout that little chiel now?"

Lucy looks down at Ellen who has fallen asleep at the

breast.

"I reckon I'll have to keep her 'til she's weaned. Should I go to see Mrs Prouse and James do you think?"

Her trepidation at the prospect of such a visit shows clearly in her face and Martha comes to her rescue.

"I'll get a message to'm through William if you like, send them your wishes."

The two women are quiet for a while then Martha gets up and takes her leave. Lucy, standing at the door with both babies in her arms and Harriet clutching at her dress, watches her walk slowly up the hill past East Furlong Farm. The church bell is tolling, its slow, sombre tones echoing throughout the village, and a thin drizzle has started to fall from a darkening sky. Remembering her washing, Lucy turns back into the cottage and closes the door with a heavy heart.

# CHAPTER TWO

It seemed to me that a sudden increase in the death rate of a small village was sure to have been worthy of news, so I set off again for the North Devon Record Office where archives of local newspapers are stored.

The *North Devon Gazette and Advertiser* is now a free tabloid paper that contains more advertisements than news. Its forerunner was the *Bideford Weekly Gazette*, established in 1854 and for over a century the main source of news for those in the Bideford area. When I was a child my family never took the *North Devon Journal-Herald*, believing it to be a "Barnstaple paper" despite its all-embracing title, but the *Gazette* was eagerly awaited every Friday. The older members of the family would always look first to "see who's died", being of an age when their contemporaries were more likely to appear in the deaths column than the births or marriages. The paper would then remain about the house for several days, being picked up by various members of the family but of no interest to myself as a small child, its huge size and small print seeming extraordinary compared to the picture books I was used to.

It was with these memories in mind, therefore, that I acquired the roll of microfilm for the *Bideford Gazette*, 1871, and loaded it on to the film reader. The first thing I noticed was the logo: the words *"The Bideford Weekly Gazette and Devon and Cornwall Advertiser"* were in the same familiar script that I remembered as a child but had now been replaced by lettering of a more utilitarian design. Below this was stated "Price One Penny." The front page consisted entirely of advertisements, both local and national, but was nevertheless dense with print, the only illustrations being three or four black and white line drawings depicting an overcoat here, a cooking stove there. The advertisements seemed curiously innocent by today's standards and made a point of naming the individual who was offering his services or wares, no doubt as a reassurance of reliability.


**"PEDLAR AND HEYWOOD,**
1, 2, 3, GRENVILLE STREET
**Return of Mr Pedlar from London**
WITH A
CHOICE AND VARIED ASSORTMENT OF
**WINTER DRAPERY GOODS**
AT EXTRAORDINARILY LOW PRICES."


**"BOOKS! BOOKS!! BOOKS!!!**
Eliza Honey Respectfully invites attention to her
Large and Varied Stock of New Books, Just Received."

There were also advertisements for

"Artificial Teeth from Mr J. Laird,
Mechanical and Operating Dentist and Chemist
Bude Street, Appledore."

And for
"Spicy, a powerful passenger paddle steam ship" which travelled between Bristol, Ilfracombe, Appledore, Bideford and Barnstaple, fare seven shillings for an "after cabin" and four shillings for a "fore cabin".
Other adverts, usually just a line or two of print, were for nationally available products, some surprisingly familiar:
"The Child's Book of Song and Praise",
"Theobromine or Concentrated Cocoa - the best without exception",
"Lea and Perrins Worcestershire Sauce",
"Rowatt's Patent Anucapnic Lamp" which "gives the

whitest flame known, without chimney, without smoke, without smell."

Enjoying this glimpse into another age, I turned to page two, imagining the rustle of old paper as I scrolled down the screen of the film reader. Here the news commenced but, unlike the aggressive headlines found in all today's newspapers, the first impression was of a daunting density of text which would surely have been intimidating in an age where literacy was an insecure skill for many people. There were seven narrow columns of small print, interspersed by occasional headlines which were in capitals but hardly larger than the main text. It was immediately apparent that all referred to national rather than local news and most concerned the Franco-Prussian War, "The War - An Armistice Offered by Prussia", "Military Funerals at Versailles." I could not imagine that farm labourers and village craftsmen, for whom education would have been a brief affair frequently interrupted by harvest and other tasks, would have taken much interest in the complex details of a war taking place in a country of which they would have had little knowledge and less understanding. Some, of course, may have had relatives in the Army or Navy, which would have encouraged greater interest in foreign countries and peoples. Even should they have wanted to read the reports however, the language used would surely have made it difficult for them.

"The capitulation of Metz is felt here as a terrible blow, for which the recent confident official assurances relative to the satisfactory position of the place left the public entirely unprepared."

I felt entirely unprepared myself after a few minutes of reading this sort of thing and could not help feeling that even the broadsheets today have lower expectations of their readers. Page three was similarly arranged in seven columns of dense print with headlines such as "The Capitulation of Metz - Full Details",

"Murder in Ireland" and
"News from Australia."

These were mixed in with advertisements for toothache cures and "Holloway's Ointment - A Certain cure for Bronchitis, Diphtheria, Sore Throat, Asthma, &c" with nothing to differentiate fact from fiction. There were also amusing tales, not of local origin, such as that of the magpie who learnt by imitation to shout "Gate ahoy!" outside a tollhouse, then went in through the kitchen window to steal food when the toll-keeper's wife went to open the gate. In true Victorian fashion the reporter of this piece could not resist moralising,

"In truth we are sorry to admit that the cleverness was so applauded that the crime was overlooked."

The fourth page was also the final one - the *Gazette* was just one folded double sheet in those days - and a quick glance indicated that this time the seven columns of print contained local news. The first column included Births, Marriages and Deaths but there were no familiar names in this issue. Below this were the High Tide Table and Hunting Appointments. Scanning the rest of the page, various headings caught my eye.

"Clovelly Herrings: - such a remarkable season as the present has, according to the belief of the oldest fishermen, never been known before".

"Northam - The Education Act - Lively Meeting - A Poll Demanded".

"The Gas Question."

"Gay Wedding", - this referred to "the rather fashionable wedding of a widow."

As on previous pages it was the formality of the language that made me smile. Under the heading "Cutting a Wife's Throat at Appledore" it was stated,

"The woman was in bed at the time and consequently on receiving this savage attack, became alarmed."

A letter to the editor making a complaint about a ploughing match at Parkham was signed "Hoping to learn that such anomalies as this are of rare occurrence, and apologising for trespassing on your valuable space, I have the honour to be, Sir, your obedient servant.*"*

Fascinating as was this voice from the past, I was not learning anything about Littleham or diseases prevalent at the time. It was likely that I would have to read through many papers if I was going to have any chance of finding useful information, so I started with the papers dating from the end of 1870 and started to search through systematically, this time turning to the last page of each paper and just scanning the local news. The first reference I found which made me sit up was a short paragraph in the edition of October 25th 1870.

"MORTALITY IN BIDEFORD: - The death rate in this town during the present month has been exceptionally high, as many as 29 names having been registered up to yesterday morning. Illness is very prevalent, and there are still many cases of fever. This disease, which has been so fatal among us during the last few weeks, is somewhat peculiar to this locality, it having been professionally termed the 'Bideford fever.'"

It seemed that I might at last have found something relevant to the deaths in Littleham. In the following week's paper there was a reply.

"MORTALITY IN BIDEFORD.
To the Editor of the Bideford Gazette.
SIR, - In a paragraph which appeared in your last issue, headed "Mortality in Bideford," it was stated that the death rate in this town during the present month has been exceptionally high, and that fever which has been so fatal amongst us during the last few weeks, was somewhat peculiar to this locality. When statements are thus publicly made which affect the interests of the town they should at least be fairly stated so that the public should not be misled by them. It is quite true that the death rate has been higher than usual, but it is not true that this has been a result of fever, as only three deaths of the 29 registered were certified to have resulted from that disease. The larger portion of the deaths

were from whooping cough and scarlatina among children, and these diseases have been very prevalent and fatal in other places besides Bideford. Your inserting the above in your next paper will oblige.

     Yours obediently,

Bideford, Oct.31st.         JAMES LEE, Registrar."

This was followed by a comment by the Editor reiterating his original point and suggesting that "fever" had been implicated in many of the deaths even if it had not been certified as causing them.

This altercation posed more questions than it answered for me. What was "fever"? Apparently not scarlet fever as scarlatina was another name for this. Could it refer to measles, diphtheria, typhoid or cholera? I knew these all commonly caused deaths in the nineteenth century. Was there any connection between the "Bideford fever" and the deaths in Littleham? The high death rate in Bideford had occurred before the increase in deaths in Littleham but this did not rule out a connection between the two. As whooping cough and scarlet fever were "very prevalent and fatal" in Bideford, perhaps these were the cause of the Littleham deaths.

I found my next clue in the issue dated December 28th 1870, just two days before Sarah Middleton died at Knowle Farm in Littleham. This was a letter from one Thomas Pynsent of Lakenham, Northam.

"THE SANITARY CONDITIONS OF NORTHAM PARISH UNDER ITS LOCAL BOARD:

Sir, - The most important duty of a Local Board is doubtless strict and unfailing attention to the sanitary requirements of the parish or district made subject to its care. I desire to consider whether this duty has been one of "primary" consideration with the Local Board which has for the past three and a half years established at Northam."

This was, of course before the days of the National Health Service and Local Health Authorities. Public health was the responsibility of newly formed local boards, which were not, if this letter was correct, always very effective. Thomas Pynsent went on to complain that within the last six months, £3,200, a huge sum at that time, had been spent on road-widening schemes to improve access to shipyards in Appledore, building schemes at Westward Ho! and "brick and tile kilns lately set up at the end of Limer's-lane." However the cost of a new well at Northam, £13 16s 10d, had been raised by the villagers, it being considered useless to apply to the Local Board. Furthermore, information as to the "sanitary state" of the area was being withheld from the Medical Department of the Privy Council lest it instigated demands for expensive improvements being made; this was despite the rising death rate, "thirty deaths from fever from the 1st October to December 21st, being twenty nine from scarlet fever and scarlatina and one from typhoid."

So, I was beginning to gain a clearer picture. It seemed that the word "fever" was used loosely to cover all kinds of infectious diseases, but also sometimes used more specifically to refer to typhoid. It was scarlet fever that was most prevalent at this time, with whooping cough and typhoid also present, and if Thomas Pynsent was correct, some of the deaths could have been prevented. It seemed that the money which should have been spent on public health was instead being spent on road improvement schemes which would benefit local businessmen. I could not help wondering whether the owners of the shipyards, building schemes and kilns were members of the Local Board.

I found a further letter from Thomas Pynsent in the *Gazette* dated January 17th 1871.

"THE SANITARY CONDITIONS OF NORTHAM PARISH UNDER ITS LOCAL BOARD
(Letter 2)
To the Editor of the Bideford Gazette.
SIR,- The last letter which I addressed to you was on the same subject and under the same heading as my present one. It appeared in the Bideford Gazette of 27th December, and

reported the mortality arising from fever in Northam parish from the commencement of the quarter on October 1st to December 21st - the date of my letter. Three weeks have since passed and next to nothing done by the local authorities to remedy the present unhappy state of things. It is true that disinfectants may be obtained gratis, and some printed information has been circulated, which some cannot and others will not read, and which few of those who do read and understand will think fit to act upon. That matters will not right themselves unaided will not be difficult to show. I would first observe that deaths from fever in Northam parish, which up to the 21st December my last letter gave at 30, at the close of the quarter ending December 31st reached 36, and I am also informed that on last Sunday afternoon, the 8th instant, there were in Appledore churchyard, at the very same time, five funerals, all resulting from deaths from fever.

To illustrate the existing state of things, I will proceed to give a short narrative of what I have learned yesterday and today relative to one family only - the inmates of one crowded cottage at Appledore. In answer to my enquiry as to the health of the place of a person well able to supply correct information, I was told that in this very cottage, where fever was raging, the corpse of a child had remained unburied for nine days; that four or five days after its decease a second child - a brother or sister of the one dead - died in the same fever-stricken cottage, and that it was not till Sunday last that the two bodies were interred: further, that two more out of the children of this family (consisting of five or six) are still most dangerously ill, and that the mother is also ill of fever - all in this small cottage. I have had these facts confirmed yesterday and today in all their essential points by four or five residents of Appledore on whose statements I can rely. Is it not then, I would ask, the duty of the constituted authorities of a parish or district to take action in the endeavour to remedy such an unhappy state of things? Private individuals, as isolated members of a Board of Health, though grieved at what they witness, are individually powerless to afford a remedy: they possess no right to interfere. Cannot, then, a Local Board, if prepared and willing to discharge its sanitary duties and be bona fide and in reality a Board of Health, do something more than leave things to right themselves and take their course on the plea that "fever is everywhere"?"

He went on to state that he believed that if action was not taken, a Medical Inspector from the Home Office would "enforce what we neglect to do" and suggested that before this should happen, a medical officer for health should be appointed to "counteract or report on the existence of anything endangering health or life."

Although he referred to Northam parish, the death rate must have referred to Northam registration district - the area in which births, marriages and deaths were registered and which comprised the parishes of Northam, Appledore, Abbotsham - and Littleham. It would seem that the whole district was affected by "fever" during the second half of 1870 and early in 1871. I continued to scan through the back pages of the *Bideford Gazette* and found the next reference to disease in the issue dated February 7th 1871. In the column reporting on the fortnightly meeting of the Bideford Local Board, was a report from the "Inspector of Nuisances, Mr Superintendent Vanstone."

"GENTLEMAN, - It having come to my knowledge that a house in Hart-street, occupied by Mrs White, has, on more then one occasion, been used as a kind of hospital for the reception of patients suffering from infectious diseases, I beg to make you acquainted with the fact, and shall be glad to know whether you wish me to take any steps in reference to the matter complained of. The case to which I now allude is that of a youth who, while suffering from scarlatina, was brought from the parish of Northam on the 19th of January, and left at the house of this woman to be nursed. It has appeared that he is not related to her in any way, and that she only took charge of him for her own pecuniary benefit. I have been spoken to with reference to this matter on several occasions, and it is the subject of general complaint that people while suffering from infectious diseases should be brought from an infected district to a thickly-populated and non-infected one, where their presence is likely to spread disease and death among the inhabitants of the locality."

On a different but not unrelated subject, he went on to state,

"I have served notice on John White, of Coldharbour, to abate nuisances on his premises which have been caused by the keeping of a pig and an accumulation of dung; but I have to report that the dung has been removed and the pig will be taken away on Friday".

His report gave rise to an "animated discussion" and other members of the board had further information to add to the report of the house in Hart Street.

"Within the last few months fever cases had been brought in from different parts of the neighbourhood, the persons being left at the house in Hart-street to be nursed and cared for. Very recently Mr B. Pickard of Northam, sent his servant - a person suffering from fever - to this nursery, and almost the last case was that of another servant in the employ of Mr Heathcote, a gentleman living in the same parish, who was brought to the house in her master's carriage."

It was suggested that all the people concerned should be "brought before the magistrates" and the Mayor asked whether "it would not be advisable to provide a suitable place for the reception of fever cases outside the town," in other words, an isolation hospital. This idea was not received with any great enthusiasm, it being felt that "persons suffering from infectious diseases should be kept in infected areas."

It was curious to read these reports and consider the changes which had taken place in intervening years; the widespread introduction of isolation hospitals; their gradual demise when antibiotics were discovered and used to control common infectious diseases; the hysteria in the early days of the A.I.D.S. epidemic when victims were shunned out of ignorance of the ways the disease could be transmitted. We seem wise when we look back at the innocence of our forebears, but if we were able to look forwards it would be apparent that it is also we who are naive. The discussion of movement of those suffering from disease, and its possible causes and methods of transmission reminded me only too forcefully of the recent outbreak of foot and mouth disease, in which we have most certainly been guilty of ignorance and lack of forethought, not perhaps excusable by our lack of knowledge.

An editorial on the same page referred to the "fever hospital" in Hart Street and suggested that if such a state of affairs was allowed to continue "we shall soon have a death rate which would be a scandal to an African village" but did not suggest any alternatives for the care of the sick.

The next reference was on March 7th, a month later when the death rate at Littleham was at its height, in another letter from Thomas Pynsent of Lakenham, entitled "The Death-Rate of Northam and the Poor of the Parish". In it he referred to the decision by the Northam Local Board, of which he was a member, not to provide a temporary isolation hospital on the grounds that the death rate did not warrant it and that it would "bear harshly upon the poor", presumably through increase of rates. He countered the first of these arguments by pointing out that the death rate for the parishes of Northam, Abbotsham and Littleham averaged 19 per quarter over the previous years, but for the quarter ending 31st December 1870 was 59, surely a sufficient increase to justify the provision of an isolation hospital even if it were only as a temporary measure.

"By looking through the county list nothing comparable to this is to be found recorded in any other district in Devon. Bideford alone comes near it... and this we find in a location blessed by nature with everything conducive to health; Atlantic breezes replete with ozone, and our towns and villages built on elevated table lands, or on slopes looking down pleasantly and healthfully on the sea or on large tidal rivers."

As I read through the letter it became apparent that Thomas Pynsent violently disagreed with his fellow members and he expressed his thoughts with utmost sarcasm. He was no doubt very unpopular but from an historical perspective it would appear that his vision was indeed more far-reaching than theirs. Already his assumption that the Government would send a Medical Inspector had been proved correct, with the arrival of one Dr Thorne-Thorne to look into the circumstances of the increased death rate in Northam and Bideford. He now reminded his fellow members of

"the untimely death of a young man, a member of their body, carried off by fever after a short illness", and addressed the second reason for the decision not to provide an isolation hospital.

"The paragraph I am commenting on further says that 'to provide a temporary hospital would bear harshly on the poor.' Well, this is a poser, and as I was the proposer of the harsh measure, I must try to defend myself from the imputed cruelty. I must confess that I had never regarded the act in this serious light before. In fact, I can go further and declare that when I have from time to time read how a Florence Nightingale had devoted her gentle life to administering to the sick and wounded in hospitals, or that an Angela Burdett-Coutts had bounteously contributed of her wealth to the support or founding of hospitals, the idea never occurred to me that they were thereby acting harshly to the poor."

In fact it is probable that it would have been the wealthier among the populace - those who were members of the Board - who would have borne the brunt of the rate increase and benefited least from the provision of a hospital. It is likely that their stated desire to protect the poor from financial demands was in reality reluctance on their part to spend money. He then referred to the fact that people suffering from infectious diseases had been sent from their homes to densely populated areas to be nursed.

"It is said that the law is powerless to punish for such an act as this. This surely is to be regretted. Let us reverse the case and consider what would be the stir were it but rumoured that the health of cattle, instead of Christian people, had been put in peril. Suppose then that a thickly-populated street ... had been so blessed as to contain a dairy farm, and that to that dairy, or to the market of the town, whilst rinderpest or the foot and mouth disease threatened the bovine race, a cow with a cold in her head, a feeling of soreness in her mouth, or tenderness in her foot, had been sent from the infected neighbouring parish, what would then have happened? Would such an act have been palliated or hushed up? Most certainly not; the bucolic mind of the squireens of all the country around would have been agitated to its lowest depths, and roused to the height of frenzy ... Wherein, then, lies the difference between rigidly protected cows and unprotected Christian people? Why, just in this - cows go to constitute cattle, and cattle is property, and may be turned into cash ... But whilst we rigorously preserve the food of man, should not man himself share a little of our solicitude? Why banish from our minds the words of Goldsmith -

"A bold peasantry, their country's pride,

When once destroyed can never be supplied,"

and why not try to guard them from fever and from all preventable diseases?"

Thomas Pynsent obviously had a strong social conscience and had apparently become a member of the Local Board for altruistic reasons, in contrast to his fellow members who seemed to be more concerned with protecting their own interests. Further letters from him appeared in the *Gazette* throughout March along with letters criticising his views and even comic poems purporting to have been written by him and by members of the Board, criticising each other. Finally there was an Editor's note;

"Mr Pynsent's correspondence on this subject must now cease."

Thomas Pynsent seemed unable to influence his associates but he must eventually have felt vindicated. The Medical Inspector, Dr Thorne-Thorne, eventually produced his report on Bideford, Northam and Appledore, which confirmed Pynsent's opinions on conditions in the latter two villages. On reading it I realised that conditions in Bideford were as bad as the neighbouring areas but there had been no maverick to complain of the Local Board's lack of action there. The report was summarised in the *Gazette* on May 9th 1871. The Editor stated that the increase in the death-rate

"was due to the prevalence of zymotic diseases, the cause of which was found to consist in the existence of abominable nuisances and an almost general excremental pollution of air, soil and water. With regard to the recent large prevalence of scarlet fever in Bideford the Inspector believes that although outbreaks of this disease cannot be clearly connected with bad sanitary conditions, yet circumstances such as those which prevailed in the borough do probably, by lowering vitality, predispose persons to receive the poison and tend to increase the death-rate. The town, he says, is one which stands in special need of every sanitary requisite, and requires constant sanitary supervision.... The worst feature at Appledore is shown to consist in the disgraceful deficiency and character of the closet and refuse accommodation, but had the town been specially designed to favour outbreaks of typhoid fever or to facilitate the spread of cholera when imported by sailors, the Inspector believes that the result could hardly have been more completely attained than has been the case here. Efforts have been made, he says, to carry out sanitary improvements, but these have no sooner been made known than strenuous and hitherto successful efforts have been made to defeat them by those who prefer the present condition of the town - a condition which in the neighbourhood seems almost proverbial - to the comparatively small pecuniary sacrifice they would otherwise have to bear."

This was obviously a thinly veiled criticism of the Northam Local Board. There followed the recommendations made by the Inspector, who stressed that,

"energetic action on the part of the Local Boards is greatly needed." They were as follows:

1. A thorough system of disinfection should be carried out wherever zymotic diseases prevail, and some special hospital accommodation should be provided for those who cannot, owing to overcrowding or otherwise, be properly cared for in their own houses.

2. The enforcement of proper ventilation in the cottages, and the closing of any which are unfit for human habitation.

3. The proper paving of all yards and courts.

4. The provision of a pure and abundant water supply.

5. The construction of an efficient system of sewerage throughout every portion of the town is urgently required. This want has for many years been felt to be of a very pressing nature, but the matter has continually been postponed, mainly owing to action taken by persons influenced by motives of a mistaken parsimony.

6.The excrement and refuse should be so dealt with as to prevent nuisance or danger to the public health. The number of waterclosets will probably greatly increase when the systems of water supply and sewerage have been carried out; but under no circumstances should the Local board tolerate the existence of closets constructed like waterclosets unless they are properly provided with water.

7.The byelaws relating to the keeping of pigs, and to the amount of open space which each new dwelling shall be required to possess, should be rigidly enforced.

8.The town stands in need of a Medical Officer of Health who should, amongst other duties, keep the Local Board constantly acquainted with the sanitary condition of the district, and give advice as to the steps by which outbreaks of disease may be best arrested and prevented."

Standards of sanitation in the Bideford area were indeed primitive when compared to our present day arrangements, but it is likely that the provisions were merely slower in being developed than in other towns; no doubt such conditions would have been normal throughout the country earlier in the century. Immediate notice was taken of the report, for Bideford was completely resewered in 1871. There was no mention of Littleham or of other surrounding villages. Might it be that conditions there were of no concern as the population consisted entirely of labourers and manual workers who, if they did become infected with disease were sufficiently isolated not to endanger the lives of the wealthier populace of Bideford? Perhaps they too needed a Thomas Pynsent to be their champion. Certainly conditions were no better in the villages. Although there was a lesser density of housing, many cottages were grossly overcrowded and it would be another eighty years before mains water and drainage reached Littleham.

It seemed certain now that the deaths in Littleham were connected with the increase in the death rate described in the newspapers. It was unlikely that it was the only rural area to be affected, as a look at the Burials Registers for neighbouring parishes proved. There was no significant increase in the death rate for the parishes of Landcross or Alwington and a slight increase in the number of child deaths in Monkleigh. The Register for Buckland Brewer however told a different story. The average number of deaths for children aged under 14 for the years 1867-9 and 1872-4 was 2.3 deaths per year. In 1870 and 1871 there were 11 child deaths each year, some occurring in the same families. It was time to verify the cause of the Littleham deaths. I chose five names from those I knew to have died in the village, all from different families and of varying ages and visited the Registration Office for Births, Deaths and Marriages in Northam. A few days later copies of their death certificates arrived in the post and I opened them with trepidation. One by one I read them.

"Scarlet fever. Certified."

"Scarlatina Maligna Abscesses Certified."

"Scarlatina Anginosa, 5 days, Certified."

"Scarlatina Maligna Certified."

"Scarlatina 3 weeks. Diphtheria 2 weeks Certified."

So there it was. Although not considered worthy of mention in the local papers except as statistics, each of these deaths would have had a profound impact on the families concerned. The death of an older relative could be expected, a part of the natural progression of things reflected in nature; a natural cycle of growth, flowering and deterioration. But the death of a child was the death of hope. I looked at the death certificate of little William Williams, described bluntly as "male, 4 years; son of William Williams, farm labourer." The "Signature, description and residence of informant" was his father, "Present at the Death." What a picture that conjured up! I noticed too that the death was registered on the very day it took place and I imagined the stricken father on his long walk to Northam, the hollow ring of his nailed boots on the hard road an echo of the emptiness he felt within.

Children do not die of scarlet fever today. Could more have been done to prevent these deaths?

# *Saturday 31st December 1870*

The familiar creak of the wooden staircase as his father descends heavily for breakfast penetrates George Glover's deep slumber. He lies still for a few moments, his limbs inert and lifeless although his mind is racing ahead into the day, then he swings out of bed in one easy movement. He reaches for his shirt and trousers in the darkness and pulls them on over his underclothes, moving quietly so as not to wake his sister Maryann who sleeps in the next bed. He picks up his boots and carefully lifts the latch and after closing the door behind him, runs down the stairs, his legs now fully awake. The room below is lit by a single candle and by the glow from the fire in the cavernous hearth where his mother crouches, pushing more sticks into the reluctant embers. She turns to him,

"You've not woken Maryann?" Standing at the table with his father, George takes up the slice of bread and dripping laid out for him.

"No, her's sleeping still." At 19, three years older than George, Maryann is now an accomplished gloveress but dislikes working by candlelight before dawn, preferring to sleep on for another half an hour and make up her time later in the day. George pushes the last of the bread into his mouth, takes a swill of black tea and bends to pull on his boots before jumping up again waving one of them in the air.

"Feyther, I've just minded, there's a nail out of my boot, can you fix'n?" He prises the sole away from the upper to demonstrate the damage. Without answering, his father wipes his thick grey moustache on the back of his hand and taking the boot and the candle, turns to the door. George follows him out into the yard, hopping with one stockinged foot. It is dark and still, with no hint of a breeze and the only sound the dripping of the thatch in the fine drizzle. His father's workshop, barely spacious enough for one man, is made smaller still by the lasts that are stacked around two walls, the hides that hang from another and the off-cuts of leather that are almost ankle deep on the floor. William Glover sweeps aside the tools on his workbench and with a few swift blows of the hammer that make the candle flicker and shadows leap, has repaired the boot and handed it wordlessly back to his son. George is perfectly capable of mending the boot himself but knows that his father likes to keep his family well shod, especially when work is in short supply as it is at this time of year.

"Are you wanting any more nails feyther? I'll make 'ee some today if I've the time." His father nods without looking up and sets about his day's work.

A few minutes later George is striding up the hill with a leather satchel containing several thick slices of bread and a piece of cheese, and a can of tea which he will heat up for dinner swinging from his hand. His home is one half of a cottage on Moorhead hill, half a mile from Littleham village. The distance by road is somewhat greater than this but by taking a short cut across fields he can avoid a climb up a steep hill. He reaches the cottage just a little way up from his own and cuts through the yard to climb a stile into Great Moor. Away from the whitewashed walls and the candlelight that gleams faintly from the window, the darkness is now complete. He enjoys the sensation of dizziness that he gets trudging forward through the blackness and sets his feet down firmly despite the swimming sensation in his head. Every now and then he closes his eyes and finding it makes no difference, wonders how it would feel to be always blind like old John Westcott who lives over the hill. Only when he senses he is approaching the first hedge does he slow down a little and holds out his hand to feel for the gate.

As he walks he is aware of two contrary moods pulling at

him. The first is familiar; he enjoys his work and his walk through the darkness is always lightened with anticipation of the forthcoming day. His first few years of fumbling and misshapen failures are over now and, although he cannot work as quickly or adeptly as his master, he understands the fire and the purpose of all the tools; he can make an adequate sickle, spade or axe; he can tyre wheels with help and make horse shoes to fit. He likes the fact that every day is different, that he never knows who will walk into the shop, what they will want to have made, what news they will bring. The knowledge that today is Saturday and the last day of the year lightens his spirits still further. He would like, tonight, to go to the village with his friend Thomas. They could have a walk around and he might perhaps see Mary, the housemaid at Higher Langdon, if she has finished her work. He feels his stomach tighten with excitement and trepidation. Afterwards he and Thomas could go in the Hoop Inn and spend a penny or two on a glass of ale. He usually gives his weekly eight shillings to his mother and has not yet asked her whether he might keep a little back.

The other mood is darker and cuts across his eager anticipation like storm clouds before the sun. Sarah, his master's youngest daughter, is ill. For the last two days Mr Dennis has been unusually preoccupied; has barely spoken except to grunt a brief instruction and George has had to talk to customers when they call, while Mr Dennis carries on working with his broad, muscled back turned. When he asks after Sarah the only response is,

"Her's bad, biy, her's bad," and he has tried to talk of other things but to no avail. When he left work yesterday evening he turned back and, fumbling with his cap in embarrassment, made himself say,

"Her'll be better soon, Mr Dennis, for sure," but the sorrowful lines that had appeared on his master's face deepened as he nodded and turned away without answering.

As he trudges across the last field George is aware of shadowy shapes, not so much a lightness as a diminution of the darkness moving away from him, and he hears a sheep coughing. He can see nothing, but the familiar ritual of the sheep bustling away from him then turning back to stare as if at something extraordinary, is so familiar that he is able to visualise it in every detail. Another anxiety distracts him. He has heard folks talking of the illness that has been spreading for some time now in Bideford, Appledore and Northam: scarlet fever, so called because the skin turns red. It's always around, when he was a child one of his friends died from it, but this time it seems worse and he has heard that whole families of children have died as a result of it in Appledore. Could that happen in Littleham? He does not know many people outside the village and whatever is happening in Bideford and Appledore has seemed as remote and inconsequential as the war going on in a place called Prussia sometimes referred to by those of his customers who can read newspapers. But for such a thing to happen here.... he feels anxiety rising from the pit of his stomach and tries to swallow it back down. Little William Williams died, and then Sarah Middleton, leaving a young baby who was now being cared for by Lucy, his brother's wife. Now Sarah Dennis is ill, bad enough to have the doctor yesterday and he knows of at least six other children who have recently caught it. But even if Sarah should die - he thinks of the smiling child who comes to the door of the forge - then surely it will stop there? His step falters as he looks towards Littleham. The village is obscured by the darkness and by the hills that rise behind it yet he can picture the little cluster of houses with their gardens of cabbages, leeks, pigsties and privies, the women laughing and gossiping in the road and the children playing on the cottage steps, the fields with the labourers carrying sacks of turnips to the bullocks, laying hedges and sowing seed. He knows every house and every face and an overwhelming affection for the place and for its people engulfs him.

"May God protect them," he murmurs, then imagines his friend Thomas overhearing him.

"Who d'you think *you* be then George, the bliddy

minister?" and he suppresses a desire to laugh.

He reaches the road at last and jumps down from the stile. The darkness has lifted a little and he increases his pace as he turns down the hill to the village. His hours are six until six, not that he ever knows the time and it is only on rare occasions that Mr Dennis takes out his pocket watch. Usually he just turns to George and, with lowered head so that he regards him through his bushy eyebrows, declares,

"Time for dinner biy" or "Time to pack up now biy." He passes the dark and silent school where he fidgeted and daydreamed for more hours than he likes to remember, calls out a "h'o there" to Mr Bowdidge carrying a lantern into his carpentry workshop at Higher Webbs and greets two workers on their way to Apps Brewery. Every morning he is glad he is who he is, George Glover, blacksmith, who has a warm forge to work in and can make things which will last almost for ever. He slows down as he approaches the track leading up to Higher Langdon and walks as tall as he can. This way he can just see the chimney of the farm and the smoke from the fire that he knows Mary has lit. Occasionally he has seen her coming down the track with two buckets to fill from the well by the roadside but he always dreads this as he does not know whether to greet her and walk on or to help with the water. Further down the hill he turns into Langdon. He sees his master is not yet out and unbolts the door of the blacksmith's shop. It is never locked. Inside it is still warm from the previous day and tying on his leather apron, he sets to work with some kindling to build up the fire again.

By midmorning there is still no sign of Mr Dennis. George has tidied the forge, sorted the nuts and bolts, twice crouched and strained to lift the anvil a few inches from the ground, ("you muz be so strong's an oss to be smith, biy"), mended an axehead for Mr Tallamy and has started on some harrow tines for Mr Heywood at Littleham Court. Every now and then he looks towards the house but he is afraid to knock at the door and intrude on whatever may be happening inside, and is unable to give any news to the several callers who come enquiring after Sarah. As he works he pretends that he has no master, that this is his own forge and people come from miles around because his work cannot be equalled. When old Mr Bale comes to warm himself and pass the time of day, George increases his pace and his voice is louder and more confident than usual as he calls out replies over his shoulder while hammering at the anvil.

"You'm growin' up fast, biy," Mr Middleton remarks as he hobbles out and George stands in the doorway with his hands on his hips in unconscious imitation of his master.

Another hour passes before he hears a horse coming into the yard and he looks out to see Mr Andrew, the curate, dismounting.

"Mornin' Mr Andrew."

"Good morning George." Mr Andrew removes his hat and shakes the rain from it. His fair curly hair has been pressed tight to his head by his hat but below that, seems to have doubled in volume with the damp weather giving him a most comical appearance. He brushes down his breeches and takes out a handkerchief and wipes his face which, despite his 47 years is as smooth as a child's.

"E's no more hair on ees face than a li'll tacker" George's father has said, their family being chapel. Mr Andrew blinks and stares at George and finally composes his face into a smile.

"Would you be so kind as to see to my horse while I call on Mr Dennis and enquire for his daughter? He has one shoe loose and I don't wish him to lose it altogether."
George takes the reins being proffered to him.

"'ow is the li'll maid, sir? I ent seen Mr Dennis this mornin'".

"She's not well, George, not well at all. I fear there may be bad news. Would you like me to give Mr and Mrs Dennis your best wishes?"

George watches him disappear into the house. Why hadn't he told Mr Andrew? Mr Dennis allows him under supervision to remove horses' shoes, rasp and measure the hooves, make new shoes and seat them, red hot and smoking, on to the hoof. One thing he has never done is to nail the shoe on. One slip, one nail just a touch out of line and the horse could be lamed. Mr Dennis was generally trusting but this was one of his few eccentricities. It was not something that could be risked, not yet, especially with a gentleman's horse. He stares at the door, willing Mr Dennis to come out and take the horse from him. He dare not knock and interrupt the dreadful scene that must be taking place inside. What could he say? But he does not know, either, what he can say to Mr Andrew if the nail is not replaced. He leads the chestnut into the forge. He is a quiet, sensible horse and nuzzles George as he lifts the hoof and examines the loose shoe. Just one nail is missing. George drops the hoof again and stands in front of the horse, stroking the velvety soft nose and feeling the warm breath on his hand. Leaving the reins hanging, he walks again to the door of the forge and stares at the house. The windows gaze back at him, expressionless and silent. The door is still resolutely shut. Beyond the house there is nothing to distract him, the drizzle has cloaked the hills and the distant church tower at Monkleigh in a grey-green mist, forcing his gaze back to closer things; to the yard where weeds grow among long forgotten wheel rims and broken ploughs, and to the empty road beyond. To his right the smoke, Mary's smoke, still curls from the chimney at Higher Langdon. He takes a deep breath and turns back into the forge.

George ties up the horse and carefully selects a nail. He runs his hand down the horse's leg and lifts the hoof, making a knee to rest it on. Bending double he lines up the nail, twisting to view it from different angles and ensure that it will run straight down the outer part of the hoof. Then taking up the shoeing hammer, he gives it two swift taps and checks again that it is straight. The horse is obliging and does not try to transfer its weight on to the lifted hoof and therefore on to George's knee. Then pausing every few seconds to ensure that the nail is true and the horse shows no sign of flinching, he hammers it home, clinches the end and smoothes it with a file.

He straightens up and wipes the sweat from his face on to his sleeve. Then untying the horse he leads it carefully forward into the yard, watching for any sign of a limp. There is none, as he knew would be the case, and he lets out a shout of triumph just as the house door opens and Mr Andrew and Mr Dennis appear. Mr Andrew's brow is wrinkled, his expression one of professional concern.

"George, little Sarah passed on a short while ago, I'm sure you'll pray for her and her family."

"Oh, Mr Dennis..."

George's throat closes up and he reaches out to his master who engulfs his hand in his huge, rough smith's hands. "You'm a good biy, George, go off off whome now, I'll close up the shop." His eyes, usually so sharp from days spent measuring and judging, are vacant and bemused, his broad frame bowed.

"I put a nail in, Mr Dennis, I was afeared to call you but I done a good job."

Mr Dennis squeezes his hand again, nearly crushing it. "Yep, you'm a good biy, take the afternoon now and I'll close up." His voice falters as he turns away, "Us'll start again next week."

Afterwards, as he walks home across the fields in the unfamiliar afternoon light, George tries to picture Sarah's closed eyes and lifeless form on the bed with her family around her but, try as he might, all he can see is the smiling child in a kaleidoscope of colour and light framed by the dark doorway of the forge as she calls her father in to dinner. He remembers again his triumph at replacing the nail successfully, - surely Mr Dennis will let him shoe a horse properly now? But he hadn't even listened and George feels aggrieved that after the years of practice and instruction, the moment when he became a fully-fledged blacksmith has been missed. But this thought is quickly and guiltily put aside as the awareness that Sarah is dead comes flooding back. He misses already the easy companionship between himself and Mr Dennis. Despite the freedom of the afternoon before him, he longs for the familiar tiredness and hunger of his usual walk home across the dark fields. The strangeness of it all stops him in his tracks and he stares out across the thickly wooded Yeo Valley below him. The rain has stopped and the far hills have reappeared in muted shades of dun and umber for the woods, green for the fields, one speckled with grazing sheep. Nothing moves. Beneath his feet the ground wheezes a little as it absorbs the earlier rain. His gaze sweeps around to the houses on Moorhead Hill, to his own house, and he imagines his parents going about their own separate business within, his father in his workshop, she perhaps sitting with her mending. His mother, he realises with a start, still does not know that Sarah is dead, that he is coming home in the middle of the day, that he has seen Mr Dennis looking so unlike himself and spoken to him. He pictures his mother's shocked expression as she puts her arms around him and he breaks into a stumbling run across the rough grass.

Later that evening he and Thomas are striding up the hill past West Furlong in the direction of the village, their footsteps drumming in unison on the rough lane. George nods in Thomas's direction.

"Bin workin' up Tansy Park again?"

"Ess. Longest hedge's all but done then just top one to lay. Be'ee gwain to be off work long?"

George has considered this. "Mother reckons Mr Dennis'll stay away 'til the li'll maid's buried, but I s'll open up Monday."

They turn a corner and ahead a circle of light floods across the road from the lantern hanging outside the Hoop Inn, intensifying the darkness outside its realm. A group of boys, a few years younger than themselves, are making use of the only light in the village to congregate, pushing each other out of the circle and falling noisily in again. One boy, his arms and legs sprouting from clothes long since outgrown, spins a stick high into the air and jumps to catch it as it spirals down until another jumps higher and wrests it from him with a loud laugh that rings out into the darkness. George slows as they approach the inn, torn between his desire to converse in a gruff voice with a pot of ale in his hand in the smoky interior of the inn, and the longing for something less defined, gentler and infinitely more disturbing which he does not quite understand, but which is summed up in one word. Mary.

"Shall us walk up to the village first?"

"Vor why? Bain't 'ee thirsty?" So they turn into the inn.

The room they enter is long, low and dimly lit. As the click of the latch announces their arrival every head turns towards the door and their progress towards the bar is closely observed. There are some eight men in the inn: the landlord James Crealock, two men sitting on high bar stools, two by the fire and three lounging on forms around a table. All, however, are facing the bar and it is clear that there has been one general conversation. Now however it is quiet until the landlord speaks.

"Thomas, George."

He puts two pots of beer on the bar and they lift them quickly, still feeling themselves to be under inspection. Finally one of the men seated by the hearth with muddy labourers' boots planted uncompromisingly each side of his stool, raises his head so that his long whiskers seem to point accusingly at George.

"Well George, you'm the *last* person us was discussing."

"Mr Middleton?" He takes another swig to hide his confusion and the room is quiet again but for the slow tick of the grandfather clock in the corner as he is scrutinised.

Another speaks. "You be'd there biy, did 'ee, when poor li'll maid passed away? Did 'ee see Mr Dennis or Mrs Dennis?"

"Ess, I see'd 'n. It were a dreadful thing..." His voice falters and there is a soft collective sigh as every man in the room looks at his boots. Gradually the conversation resumes, as all preceding and subsequent events are lingered over. Only William Piper, who at 81 is too deaf to take part, is silent and sits by the fire staring at the floor, an odd figure who would have looked more at home in the eighteenth century with his long, grey, straggly hair and dark-coloured smock frock. It is remembered by one that Mr Dennis lost another daughter named Sarah many years ago, by another that scarlet fever had "carried very many away" back in the fifties. Best to put them all in bed together so they catch it and be done with it, suggests one man with a long gloomy face, as he taps his pipe out on to the table. Might as well, agrees another, for it costs too much to call the doctor.

"'Tis one rule for the rich and another for the poor." With this comfortingly familiar philosophy, the room again subsides into silence but for the occasional crack from the fire as a flame flares and dies.

The landlord, a tall man with a slight stoop, refills the boys' mugs and takes their proffered coins. There are some evenings when no money crosses the bar, many of the men quietly placing a rabbit, a pheasant or a few eggs on the bar when they enter, or a small bag of turnips, potatoes or corn for the landlord's chickens on the floor by the door. If these gifts are legitimate, the donor will boast of his best ever potato crop or the multitude of rabbits on Lower Boundstone Farm that he is allowed to snare as extra payment. Often though the gifts are given silently and never acknowledged except by the passing of pots of beer, these being the goods that the employer or hardworking wife "will never miss". Even those who work at Apps Brewery and have an allowance of a gallon of beer a day, find something to barter for an extra pint in the evening.

James Crealock pours some beer for himself and lights his pipe, repeatedly sucking the flame down into the bowl until it burns to his satisfaction whereupon he places it on the bar, thrusts his thumb into his waistcoat and rocks on his heels.

"Course they've had it terrible down Appledore way. Ever so many have died down there. A gentleman writing in the paper says they've catched it from the heaps of rummage lying about."

"They've allus bin a muxy ol' crowd down Appledore,"

interjects a wizened little man in the corner, whose darkened skin is surely, at this time of year, the result of unfamiliarity with water rather than acquaintance with the sun.

"Ess, they'm not Christian down there," puts in another. "I've yeard the dead and the dying all lie in together with no one to minister to them. You know for why? 'Cos the wife is down some court, tipsy on gin!"

"They eat nought but fish, so 'tis no wonder."

James Crealock picks up his pipe again and sucks on it affectionately. "The gentleman wrote as it should be a *Minister* as clears up the muck," heads turn towards him, open-mouthed, "or, I should say, order for it to be done."

"Wull," puts in the gloomy looking man, "they've brought it on theirselves, that's all I can say. Us won't get it bad like that up yur."

"If that's the case" says another, "why has us got it at all?"

From the hearthside, either because the drift of the conversation has penetrated his deafness or his thoughts have independently carried him that way, William Piper mutters, "Death respects no man." At this apparent truth, the room falls into a subdued silence.

George gazes down into his mug and swills the dregs of his beer around and around. The conversation has too gloomy a tendency for him and his thoughts begin to turn to other things that he can find neither words nor images to illustrate but which exercise a powerful hold on his emotions. Thomas has now struck up a conversation with another of the farm labourers at the bar, discussing the merits of the new plough that Mr Heywood bought last year and barely notices when George nudges him with a "I'll see 'ee later" and heads for the door.

Outside, the pool of light illuminates an empty lane. It is dry and still and as he moves into the darkness he sees stars and knows that the sky has cleared. A tawny owl cries from Narracombe; an abrupt, penetrating "keewick" which is repeated, then answered by a softer, quavering "who-oo-oo-oo" from further down the valley. There is no other sound except the trudge of his boots, then the snuffling and grunting of a pig behind the cottages at Lower Webbs. He reaches the crossroads where the signpost gleams palely and turns down the hill. When he reaches the track to Higher Langdon he stops and gazes up the banked hedge which obscures the farmhouse above. The chimney is as dark as the sky, the smoke invisible. A cow shifts and moans quietly from the byre.

He walks back up the road and this time turns right. He scarcely knows why, but is reluctant to return to the inn. He hesitates outside East Furlong Cottages where his brother William and wife Lucy live. Little Harriet's face always lights up when she sees him but she will be in bed now and he does not want to mull over the day's events again. A clock strikes as he passes the farmhouse but his mind is too numb to count the hour. From Mount Pleasant comes a voice, then an answer and a closing door. Quick footsteps proceed down the lane towards him. He does not feel capable now of even uttering a greeting and steps aside into the shadow of the hedge. The slight figure is almost upon him, walking fast with the swish of a heavy skirt, the shadow of a bonnet. As she passes something familiar makes him step forward.

"Mary?"

She lets out a little shriek and clutches her shawl around her. "Who's that?"

He sees the outline of her features and knows with a rush of excitement that it is indeed she.

'Tis only I, George. May I walk with 'ee?"

She regains her composure. "If 'ee want to, I don't care."

They walk in silence with the breadth of two people between them. George draws a deep breath and realises that he is shaking.

"'Ave 'ee been out callin'?"

"Ess. I looked in to see Mrs Grigg and taked her some eggs from Mrs Tallamy. Her li'll maid be bad now. I'n't it turrible 'bout Sarah Dennis?" She turns to him, remembering his part in the drama.

"Ess. Mr Dennis was took turrible bad s'mornin'." He draws himself up a little. "I s'll run the shop next week."

"Oh." She throws him an admiring glance. They continue in silence, their footsteps ringing in the stony lane, one of his for every two of hers. George is bursting with things he wants to say but cannot find words for. As they approach the track to Higher Langdon he slows, tense with fear that she will continue home without pausing but she too reduces her pace until they stand, still distant. He is intensely aware of her smallness beneath her shawl and feels himself to be awkward and clumsy.

"Be'ee walkin' tomorrow?"

"Maybe, maybe not." She turns away from him slightly but adds helpfully, "'Tis my afternoon off."

He hardly dares say it but steels himself. "Can I walk with 'ee?"

"If 'ee want to, I don't care." But then she flashes him a quick smile, as if acknowledging that this is a game and that it is his turn to play the next card.

"Shall I meet 'ee yur then?"

"If you like." And suddenly she is gone, her quick footsteps almost running up the track.

George stands staring up the track into the darkness. Then, elated, he turns and walks back the way he has come, blindly past the inn, down the hill and up again towards his cottage without knowing where he is going or why, feeling that his feet are hardly touching the ground and haunted by an ecstatic kaleidoscope of images and snatches of talk that keep him awake long after he is in bed and then invade his dreams and carry him out of the old year and into the new.

# CHAPTER THREE

Today scarlet fever is a disease of which one rarely hears. Those who are now in their fifties and sixties remember that it was still taken seriously in their childhood, no doubt because its past severity was still fresh in many memories; mothers were fearful if it was contracted and some children were confined in isolation hospitals until fully recovered. Today however children are not immunised against scarlet fever and it is not often that a parent speaks of her child having caught it.

It is caused by a streptococcal infection of the throat and is spread by droplet infection or contaminated milk or food. It has an incubation period of two to four days. If it is contracted it generally causes a sore throat and a mild fever followed by a rash, the whole episode being over within a week and rarely causing complications. So what has changed? In the nineteenth century there were no antibiotics available to treat possible complications but in any case these are rarely needed today in the management of scarlet fever. It would seem that the reason for the transformation lies in a combination of social factors and changes in the disease itself. I started to read books about the history of disease and medicine to try and discover why so many had died in Littleham.

Infant mortality was high throughout the nineteenth century. One half of all children of farmers, labourers, artisans and servants died before their fifth birthdays, the number of deaths being greater in city slums than in rural areas. Scarlet fever was a major cause of death in the second half of the nineteenth century; the mortality rate doubled between 1840 and 1870. It was the most common cause of death in children over the age of one and was feared so much it was often referred to simply as "the fever" - this accounted for the confusion I had experienced when reading some of the newspaper reports. Undoubtedly many children, and particularly those of poor parents, had less resistance to disease than children do today. Houses were usually overcrowded with families of eight or ten sleeping in one or two bedrooms; diets were inadequate, consisting largely of bread or potatoes, - protein, usually in the form of bacon or cheese, was scarce and was often kept for the man of the household so that he had the strength to continue working and earn a wage for his family; hygiene was poor as all water had to be fetched from a pump, well or stream and was sometimes contaminated; toilet facilities were either located in primitive earth closets outside or were non-existent and open sewers ran through the streets; refuse collection was, at best, inadequate. It is clear from the reports in the *Bideford Gazette* that these conditions were all present in the Bideford area and certainly accounted for an increased susceptibility to disease, but the virulence of the disease itself was also greater than at present.

The deaths from scarlet fever in the second half of the nineteenth century were caused by a severe form of the disease sometimes called septic or malignant scarlet fever. The infection was so overwhelming that it could lead to septicaemia or blood poisoning, with the symptoms of high fever, shivering, headache, rapid breathing and sometimes delirium. The infection could then be carried in the blood to different parts of the body such as the heart valves, brain or liver. An even greater danger was the effect of the toxins on the walls of blood vessels, causing severe damage so that fluid was lost into the tissues. The loss of fluid was such that normal circulation could not be maintained and the patient would go into shock, showing symptoms of collapse, a rapid, weak pulse and pallor. The failure of blood supply to all parts of the body would then rapidly lead to failure of the liver, lungs, kidneys and brain. There was no effective medication to halt the onslaught of the infection and children could die within a few days of the first symptoms.

By the end of the nineteenth century, deaths from scarlet

fever were decreasing. This was not due to improvements in treatment as no effective therapies were developed until the discovery of antibiotics in the 1930's. Rather, the disease itself reduced in severity coupled with improvements in public health and the general health of the population.

Of course, scarlet fever was not the only hazard for children in Victorian Britain. Babies commonly died from "atrophy" and stomach disorders, both of which could be attributed to poor nutrition and lack of hygiene. Overcrowding and efforts to keep babies quiet could lead to death through "overlaying" or suffocation while sharing the parents' bed, or, more sinisterly, through administration of opiates. Laudanum or Godfrey's cordial, both containing opium, were commonly given to babies to keep them quiet, especially in families with absent fathers where the mother was forced to take in work in order to earn a living or to leave the baby with a minder while she worked in the fields. The death rate was particularly high amongst illegitimate babies for this reason.

From my window as I write I see a small girl of six or seven walk importantly up the road towards the post box outside my house, her concentration evidence of the solemnity of her mission. She traces the wording on the post-box with slowly moving finger, her lips moving hesitantly, before reaching up on tiptoe to push her letter in. Turning away, a hop breaks in to her determined walk and after a few more paces she is unable to contain her energy any longer and she skips towards her house and into her future. Her mother may have vague fears related to her safety but she would never expect to lose her daughter through illness. Fortunately most of us today never see serious illness in children; indeed for many of us our only acquaintance with illness and death is with the more easily accepted afflictions of the elderly, though of course it is a very different story in the Third World. It is hard for us to imagine what it must be like to be forever watching our children for signs of ill health. A simple sore throat might be a sign of scarlet fever or the equally deadly diphtheria; a stomach upset might be cholera or typhoid. Measles, whooping cough and tuberculosis caused many deaths, as did smallpox in the first half of the nineteenth century. Of course many children recovered from these diseases though some were so weakened by the infection that they had little resistance when the next one came along. One of the death certificates I obtained stated:

"Scarlatina 3 weeks. Diphtheria 2 weeks."

For the parent of a sick child there were many medical interventions that could be tried, if few which had any appreciable effect. Morphine was freely available, as was opium, usually in the form of laudanum where it was mixed with alcohol. This acted as a sedative, painkiller and cough suppressant but had no effect on infections. Patent medicines were available from grocers, chemists and by post; many contained a high proportion of alcohol and all made extravagant claims of their effectiveness. J. Collis Browne's Chlorodyne, advertised as a cure for coughs, colds, colic, cramps, spasms, stomach-ache, bowel pains, diarrhoea and sleeplessness, contained morphine, chloral hydrate, and cannabis. Many parents relied on home cures and herbal remedies and might give cowslip wine for measles, bread poultices to reduce swelling, onion tea for sore throats or a heated shallot in the ear for earache. In some parts of the country it was even the practice to eat a fried mouse as a cure for whooping cough. Home remedies at least had the advantage over patent remedies that they cost little or nothing but the sad fact was that there was little that could be done to halt a virulent infection.

Advice was issued to the public in the hope of limiting the spread of infection. While reading the *Bideford Gazette*, I found the following recommendations in the issue of 8th November 1870.

"SCARLET FEVER.

1. If a case of scarlatina, or scarlet fever, or bad sore throat appear in your house, send immediate information to the

Local Board of Health.

2. If possible separate the patient immediately from the rest of the inmates. A room at the top of the house is, as a rule, the best sick room.

3. Let the room in which the patient lies be stripped of all carpets and curtains.

4. Let all discharges of whatever kind be received on their very issue from the body into a disinfectant, such as Calvert's powder, chloride of lime, carbolic acid, or Condy's fluid.

5. Let small pieces of rag be used instead of pocket-handkerchiefs for wiping the mouth and nose, each piece after being once used should be immediately burnt.

6. About the fourth day of the eruption let the body be well rubbed with camphorated oil twice a day, the oiling to be continued until the patient is able to take a warm bath, in which the whole skin should be well scrubbed with disinfecting carbolic acid soap.

7. Ten days after health is quite re-established the patient may in clean clothes re-enter the family.

8. A large vessel containing Condy's fluid, in the proportion of one ounce to every gallon of water, should be kept in the room. All bed and body linen on its removal from the person of the patient to be immediately placed therein.

9. Attendants on the sick should be scrupulously clean, and frequently wash their hands with a disinfectant.

10. In case of death, the corpse should be sprinkled with a disinfectant, and speedily buried.

11. No child having had the scarlet fever should be allowed to re-enter a school without a certificate from the medical attendant, stating that he can do so without risk to the others.

12. On the recovery or removal of a patient, all floors, walls and ceilings should be fumigated, scraped and cleaned. For fumigating infected rooms and their contents nothing is better than sulphur. A quarter of a pound of brimstone, broken into small pieces, should be put into an iron dish (or the lid of an iron saucepan turned upside down), supported by a pair of tongs over a bucket of water. The chimney and other openings

are then closed with paper pasted on, and a shovelful of live coals is put upon the brimstone. The door is then quickly shut, the crevices covered with paper and paste, and the room kept closed for five or six hours. After this a thorough cleansing should be effected; everything washable should be washed, and all other things should be cleansed by proper means.

13. It is highly dangerous to send a child to any school, public or private, from any house or family in which fever exists.

14. In localities where the fever is very rife, all day and Sunday schools should be temporarily closed.

15. Any person suffering from any dangerous infectious disorder who wilfully exposes himself in any public place or public conveyance, and anyone in charge of such person, and any owner or driver of a public conveyance who does not immediately disinfect his conveyance after conveying an infected person, or who, without previous disinfection, gives, lends, sells or transmits (to the wash or otherwise), any bedding, clothing, linen or rags which have been exposed to infection is liable to heavy penalties."

It is hard to see how anyone living in overcrowded accommodation could carry out these instructions, even supposing they had access to a copy of the local paper, were able to read it and had the means to buy all the requirements. A large family on a low income would have found this difficult at the best of times and perhaps impossible when stricken with illness. Some labourers' families with six or seven children were living in two bedroomed terraced cottages in Littleham in 1871. With so many sleeping in just two bedrooms, how could anyone suffering from an infectious illness possibly have been isolated and how could any medicines be afforded?

The advice given in the *Bideford Gazette* was advanced for its time. Throughout the Victorian era the most commonly held theory of disease transmission was that of miasmas, the belief that diseases were caught from noxious odours emanating from rotting organic matter, so that anyone passing an unpleasant-smelling compost heap or cesspit was in danger of catching a disease simply by inhaling. Diseases believed to be transmitted this way were known as zymotic diseases because they were thought to be caused by zymosis or fermentation. This belief, although flawed, led to many improvements in public health because as the sources of bad smells, in the form of refuse and open sewers were removed, so too the risk of typhoid or cholera from bacterial infection decreased. The miasmic theory remained current for longer than it perhaps would otherwise have done as the action taken as a result of the theory led to improvements in health, even though the reasons for this were misunderstood.

An opposing and, we now know, more realistic theory was put forward as early as 1849, suggesting that cholera was caused by an organism or bacteria which multiplied in the intestine. This was rejected, as was Pasteur's Germ Theory in 1861. Most people could not understand how disease could be transmitted by something that could not be seen, and miasmas could at least be smelt. Gradually however the idea gained hesitant acceptance from some practitioners. In the 1860's Joseph Lister began using disinfectants during surgery with the aim of killing bacteria; until that time surgeons would move from one operation to another, or from an autopsy to a birth without washing the blood from their hands. Perhaps not surprisingly mortality rates following surgery were high but Lister was able to demonstrate a fifty per cent decrease in mortality through using disinfectant. Most doctors ridiculed the germ theory and it was not until 1870 that it was more generally accepted and the use of antiseptics became more widely used, but the advice given in the *Bideford Gazette* in 1870 would still have seemed unusual to many people. By the 1890's bacteria had been identified with the use of microscopes and enough scientific research carried out to prove the theory and the belief in miasmas died out.

If the advice given in the *Bideford Gazette* had been closely followed, as it could have been in an isolation hospital, there is no doubt that the transmission rate of the disease would have been greatly decreased. In an overcrowded cottage however, it was little more than useless. It would be another 16 years before Bideford had a purpose-built hospital; the infirmary ward at the workhouse would have been an inadequate alternative. There was also little that a visiting doctor could do. He had no medicines that could significantly alter the course of an infection and could only offer a tonic in the form of cod liver oil or iron and, less usefully, a laxative, usually senna or calomel, which one can only assume would further weaken the patient. It is likely however that any medicines ordered by the doctor would have had a powerful placebo effect as most people had considerable faith in his abilities. He could also, of course, offer a diagnosis, reassurance and advice on caring for the patient and this must have been preferable to no visit at all for the frightened mother of a sick child.

The poorest families would not have been able to afford to call out the doctor. His fees varied according to the means of his patients; the wealthy might pay a guinea for a visit; for others the normal fee might be nearer five shillings although doctors often only charged one shilling and sixpence when they knew that their patients were unable to pay more. Even this would have been beyond the means of the poorest people. A farm labourer would have earned about ten shillings a week; in a family with several children there would have been days when there was barely a crust to eat and certainly nothing left over for such luxuries as doctors. As the cost of calling out the doctor was so prohibitive, many families would try home remedies first and only send for him when all else had failed, by which time it was often too late for the little advice he could offer.

Although it would be many years before the National Health Service would be established, there was some provision for the poorest people in society. As early as the sixteenth century there was an understanding that society had some responsibility for the destitute or the "deserving poor" as they were sometimes called. Following the Poor Law Act of 1601, later known as the Old Poor Law, Overseers of the

Poor were appointed in each parish who were responsible for seeing that the sick and destitute were provided with basic necessities in the form of money or food. These were supplied from rates paid by those of sufficient means and were distributed in the vestry of the parish church. Over the next two hundred years there were various amendments to the act, usually made in an attempt to reduce costs as the number of people requiring relief at some time in their lives remained very high, especially as the population and unemployment rose and the cost of bread increased. Parishes were allowed to set up poor houses or workhouses if they wished, as it was cheaper to support families and individuals in this way rather than paying for their rent and keep individually. However costs continued to rise until in 1834 the Poor Law Amendment Act or New Poor Law was established. This recommended that there should be one system for the whole country, in which parishes should join together to form unions and each union build a workhouse for all its paupers. There was no longer any aid for people in their own homes but all were required to enter the workhouse if they wanted help; this was known as the Workhouse Test - those who refused to enter the workhouse were refused any form of aid.

The workhouse was universally feared for the regime was inhuman in its severity. The standard of living had, by law, to be below that of the poorest paid labourer - and he barely survived on starvation rations. The views of the Reverend H. Milman, reporting to the Royal Commission, were typical of many:

"The Workhouse should be a place of hardship, of coarse fare, of degradation and humility; it should be administered with strictness, with severity; it should be as repulsive as is consistent with humanity."

It was indeed. Families were separated, husbands from wives and even parents from children, none were allowed any contact while within the workhouse. Personal clothing was removed and the inmates made to wear shapeless uniforms of coarse cloth. Rules were strict and the daily routine dull and repetitive; all paupers were required to work at such tasks as sack making, stone-breaking or laundry work. Yet access was restricted to the "deserving poor", those who were unable to support themselves due to old age, illness or lack of a major bread winner in the family; the unemployed and those receiving very low wages were considered the able-bodied poor and were the target of much criticism.

Critics of the New Poor Law sometimes referred to it as the "concentration system", a term which carries sinister undertones today. Comparisons with the concentration camps of Nazi Germany are not far fetched. One critic in the 1850's, quoted by Ruth Richardson, referred to poor people being

"used as though they were not of the same species as those who crowded them into passages, and pushed and drove them like so many sheep and oxen."

The treatment meted out inside the workhouse was enough to spread fear throughout the community yet there was another threat that led some families to take extreme avoiding action. In 1832 the Anatomy Act had been passed, making the corpses of paupers dying in workhouses, and others in the wider community too poor to pay for funerals, available for dissection. The demand for corpses, used in medical training, had been met by the bodies of murderers being passed from the gallows to the anatomy schools as an added punishment. This undoubtedly had some preventative effect for there was a widespread fear of dissection which was seen to fly in the face of all respect and religious ritual due to a loved one's remains. As demand for medical training increased, the gallows proved an insufficient source and a lucrative trade in grave robbery developed, culminating in the crimes of Burke and Hare who did not wait for their victims to die, but murdered them and sold the corpses to anatomy schools. It was partly the public outcry following the disclosure of their crimes that led to the Anatomy Act being passed but this time it was not murderers whose bodies were dissected but those whose only crime was poverty.

The fear of dissection, when added to the inhumane

regimes of the workhouse, was enough to prevent any who could avoid it from entering. Yet even those who died at home were not safe if their relatives could not afford to pay for a funeral. It is known that some bodies were kept for many days before a request for a pauper funeral was made, in order that decomposition was too far advanced for dissection to be carried out. It is not impossible that those who kept the bodies of their children for days in overcrowded cottages in Appledore were protecting them from what was seen as the ultimate indignity, though I was unable to find any evidence of local dissections.

The Bideford Union Workhouse was built in Meddon Street in 1836 for two hundred inmates. It was as much feared as any workhouse and many poor people dreaded ending their days there, seeing such a fate as a source of shame as well as privation. Even in the 1960's and 1970's, many years after the Bideford workhouse had been converted to a hospital, I can remember elderly relatives being very reluctant to enter the geriatric wards there as they still saw it as the "work'us" despite the high standard of care offered. In 1997 the site was taken over by the Devon and Cornwall Housing Association, the old workhouse converted to thirteen flats and the land behind renamed Union Close as a reminder of its origins and developed for housing.

As the nineteenth century progressed there was much criticism of the inhumanity of the Poor Law and this, coupled with the rising costs in the workhouses, led many Unions to reintroduce some "outdoor relief" - giving aid to people in their own homes. This was especially common in rural areas where agricultural employment was seasonal and casual workers were laid off when the weather was bad or there was little work. It was cheaper to keep a family in their own home and pay them an allowance when there was no work, than to move them to the workhouse for the entire year. It was however commonly seen as a source of great shame to have to apply to the Union for aid and many people came near to starvation rather than do so.

This, then, was the situation in 1871. In Littleham those who could not afford to pay for a doctor's visit could apply to the Union for aid. This would have involved walking three miles each way to Bideford, frequently with a return visit the next day to see whether the request had been granted. If and when the doctor finally arrived he might recommend medicine which would then have to be obtained from the Union, but as many unions had limited supplies of medicines, doctors would often order food and drink to be given as a tonic. Pamela Horn in her book *"The Victorian Country Child"* gives instances of unions providing eggs, milk and meat to children and even of children as young as ten being given half a pint of brandy a week while recovering from fever. It may be that these measures were as efficacious as the rather ineffectual medicines then available.

Those who were reluctant to apply to the Union for help or whose requests were refused might be helped by charity. In many villages the local gentry or clergyman would visit the sick with gifts of food, medicines, clothing or fuel. Some clergy made a speciality of caring for the sick and kept a store of medicines and home remedies for the purpose. In *"Rural Life in Victorian England"*, the author G.E. Mingay cites the eccentric Reverend Sydney Smith as a prime example; he claimed to perform miracles in his parish by treating whooping cough with garlic but even he met his match when an epidemic of scarlet fever hit his village, carrying away 15 of his parishioners;

"You will naturally suppose I have killed all these people by doctoring them, but scarlet-fever awes me and is above my aim."

In many towns and villages there were also charitable bequests made to the poor, to be distributed by the overseers or the clergy. In Littleham the sum of £16 10s had been bequeathed at some unknown time to the poor of the parish; during the nineteenth century the interest on this sum, amounting to 16s 6d, was distributed each Christmas "among such of the poor labourers of the parish, as do not receive constant relief."

There was another alternative available to those who could afford it - membership of a local friendly society. These operated as an early form of insurance company; members paid a small sum each week and were then able to claim a weekly amount and medical fees if unable to work through illness or accident. Some societies restricted membership to certain trades while others were open to anyone within a geographical area, but many would only extend benefits to the named member - usually the man of the household - so were no help for the treatment of sick children. It is little surprise then that illness was so greatly feared in the nineteenth century, when access to health care was unavailable to many and of limited benefit to those who could afford it. We may be critical of the National Health Service today but it is worth remembering the plight of our ancestors when we next telephone for a doctor's appointment.

Despite these difficulties a doctor did, no doubt, make many visits to Littleham in 1871. Who might he have been? There was of course no doctor living in Littleham, there being no professional people among the population, but in Morris' Directory for 1870 there are six doctors listed in Bideford, one being the surgeon at the Union Workhouse. Their households are detailed in the 1871 census; most had three live-in servants and lived at prestigious addresses in the town centre - the town had not of course spread much beyond the centre at that time. Three were additionally Justices of the Peace and two were trustees of the Bridge Estate. Two doctors, William Ackland and Richard Hoyle, lived at addresses in Bridgeland Street and ran the dispensary on the Quay. The dispensary, situated in the building now occupied by the Portman Building Society, was supported by voluntary contributions; subscribers donated an amount of money each year and in exchange could name a certain number of people they wished to be given free treatment, perhaps in some cases their servants. Dr William Ackland was a close friend of Charles Kingsley and is mentioned several times in Susan

Chitty's book "*Charles Kingsley's Landscape*". He was "a man after Kingsley's own heart . . . he was deeply concerned for the welfare of the working classes, and particularly concerned with the state of their drains." He enlisted Kingsley's help during a cholera outbreak in Bideford in 1854 and they remained lifelong friends. Might it have been he who rode the three miles of rough tracks to Littleham on cold winter nights in 1871? It would seem that no records remain to tell us.

# *Thursday 19th January 1871*

Martha Powe sighs as she shakes the sheet on to the table in the Rectory sewing room. Her mind is not on her work, but she is an accomplished seamstress and her hands work swiftly as if independent of the rest of her body. She takes up the scissors and cuts straight down the middle of the sheet, pushing the blades against the taut material so that they slide as if through butter. With a quick, nervous gesture she pushes back a lock of straight, dark brown hair that has escaped from the tightly coiled bun at her nape then turns the two pieces of sheet, shakes, folds and starts to pin them together. Her head aches and every sinew in her body feels tight, as if it might snap if put under any more pressure. Why has she come? She is needed so much more at home. The ways in which she is needed crowd in on her again and with another sigh she tries to push them aside and concentrate on her work. She takes up four more pins and holds them between thin compressed lips while she smoothes and folds the two pieces of sheet together. This sheet is from Elizabeth Blackmore's bed. She knows all the linen, having put in every stitch herself. She would have made this one for the children's beds, Master John or Master Charles perhaps when they moved from their cradles. When it grew thin it was moved to the servants' linen cupboard and used until the centre threatens to tear. Cut and turned it will last a few more years. Taking up the sheet she seats herself by the window and threads her needle.

The Rector is away again, he and Mrs Harding both in London on business and only the children and servants left. It isn't right, he should be in his parish now, although what he could do she couldn't imagine. That's what makes it so hard, what can anyone do? First William Williams, then Sarah Middleton - a grown woman - then Sarah Dennis taken so quickly. Now her Elizabeth is ill - but that's different, there are plenty that have the fever but most will recover. Please let her recover. Elizabeth Hockin has come in to look after her today and she knows better than anyone how to care for sick children. Martha gazes unseeingly out of the window and her eyes fill with tears as she remembers how kind everyone is, the offers of help, the little presents. Last evening Maria Westcott had come bustling in carrying a pudding, just as if she knew Martha had not even thought of supper. *And* she had stayed to sweep the floor. Whereas William - Martha remembers with irritation how her husband had come cheerfully through the door with his "Everything all right then?" just after Maria left. He just doesn't know. He has no idea how she is feeling. She pulls aggressively at the thread, then has to smooth out the puckers she has made in the sheet. This morning he ate his breakfast as calm as anything while she flew around the kitchen, tidying, sweeping, coaxing the fire, taut from lack of sleep. He could have fetched the water! He knew that she too had to be at the Rectory today but left with a smile and not even an offer of help. And he never woke when Elizabeth cried. Her anger rises and she glares at the wall as she silently shrieks the uncompromising truth,

"You think of nothing but yourself and your horses! You care for them more than your wife and children! I hardly slept last night but *you* never notice do you!" She imagines his guileless brown eyes clouding with misery and feels vindicated and somewhat ashamed.

She gazes out of the window at the church tower and her eyes travel up to the turrets that are silhouetted against a steely sky. She is thankful the bell is not tolling today as it was two weeks ago, each knell falling deeper within her, and the wait for the next like the silence that comes between dying breaths. She had looked up from her sewing each time she heard the church gate creak and had seen her silent neighbours coming in ones and twos with slow steps and downcast eyes. Finally she had put down her work and throwing on her black shawl had hurried to join them, just gaining her seat at the back of the church before she heard the slow, matched tread of the bearers and Ann Dennis's heartbreaking sobs as she followed her daughter's coffin. She feels her eyes filling with tears again as she imagines herself in Ann's place. Mr Andrew had stood there in the pulpit telling them all that Sarah's death was God's will, that He in His infinite wisdom had chosen to release her from a world of suffering and sin and to give her parents the opportunity to learn submission to His will. Ann Dennis had continued to shake with grief and her husband stood hunched beside her with bowed head as if in fear of further blows from above. How could they think of Sarah's death as a release from a sinful, sorrowing world when the child had been the most joyful, smiling creature you could hope to meet? How could they ever see it as anything but a punishment for some unknown thoughtless act they had themselves committed? Yet Ann Dennis is a wonderfully religious woman and it is said - for her tears, utterances and fluctuations of mood are the subject of daily concern in the village - that at times she is already able to thank God for Sarah's life and look forward to a time when they will meet again.

Martha leans forward to see the little grave, looking even smaller now that the earth is settling. She knows that if it were her child down there, she would be overcome with bitterness and anger and would never be able to thank God for taking her, even though she prays in church for a more humble, forgiving nature. She shakes the thought out of her head. Elizabeth is going to be all right. Many children survive the fever. The tension eases a little from her shoulders as her eyes move over the familiar green contours of the churchyard which gather round the uncompromising strength of the solid little church and its modest tower. The wind has strengthened during the morning and as the clouds shift and change, a little weak sunlight glints on the weathervane that shivers above the tower.

Usually she enjoys her Thursdays at the Rectory. She looks forward to seeing the pile of work laid out for her and is glad when there is variety in the tasks. She loves the silence of the little room, the clear whiteness of the walls, her chair by the window, and the sewing box with its row of needles, bright pincushions and threads of more colours than you could have imagined. At dinnertime she goes down to the kitchen, guessing the meal from the aroma on the backstairs. There are usually eight around the table. She counts them, matching their names with her stitches as her needle darts in and out. The three Elizabeths who live in as cook, parlour maid and housemaid, little Mary Shute, the gardeners William Newcombe and William Short, and her husband William. He is the groom and also doubles as the butler when the Rector is home. Usually the meal is good-humoured, sometimes uproarious when the Rector is away from the house. But today there will be no amusing stories or ribald humour for the talk will all be of fever. Most people are touched in some way by illness and all are fearful.

Her thoughts fly back to her home and the seven-year-old girl sick upstairs. Elizabeth slept poorly, and when she did sleep often cried out at the pain in her throat. Martha has spent more time soothing her and stroking her hot forehead than she has in her own bed. Mary and William are old enough to help Mrs Hockin and keep an eye on five-year-old Ellen, but she knows they are frightened by their sister's illness. Will Mary be back home yet? Martha has told her to walk to Bideford to buy Condy's fluid, repeating the instructions again and again and gesticulating with the knife as she cut the bread,

"*Up* along High Street, no *High* Street, you know, where us gets ribbons and so forth but not so far as that, then *right* along Mill Street, *past* the baker's and then it's on your left."

Mary has never been to town on her own before and is not used to asking for things in shops. Martha has made her write "Condy's fluid" in big letters on a scrap of paper so that she will not have to say anything at all, but she is so timid that there is no certainty that she will even dare to go into the shop. As bad as her father when he was young, he could never say boo to a goose and is not much better now. She is good with her hands, however, and already almost a match for Martha when it comes to sewing; there will be no difficulty in finding a position for her next year, hopefully in Pedlar and Heywood's or one of the other drapers in town. That is where the future is these days. Surely she must be home by now? Martha wishes she had asked Ellen to run down with a message so that she would know. *She* would have no problems with shyness, she is a proper madam already and quite capable for five years old; today she is going to peel the potatoes for Mrs Hockin. William, however, was pale and quiet this morning, his usual grin subdued by anxiety and she hadn't the heart to set him to work. He is a good boy, usually willing to help her, though easily distracted by schemes of his own. She smiles as she remembers the time she had slammed impatiently out of the house looking for the water she had asked him to fetch, only to find that he had not yet gone but was trying to construct a yoke from pieces of firewood and rope. But he *must* help her tonight. There is so much to do! Dr Ackland said the dung heap must be moved on account of the bad air, but with the evenings being so dark how can it be done before Saturday? Could she and William do it tomorrow? He will at least be home, for none of the children must go to school until the fever is quite gone.

She cuts the thread, folds the sheet and picks up a stocking that needs darning. Miss Josephine's from the look of it. If she had to darn her own stockings perhaps she would cut her toenails more often. A movement in the yard below catches her eye and she looks down to see the housemaid, Elizabeth Blackmore, vigorously shaking out her duster then relaxing and gazing vacantly around her before returning into the house. Martha hears the rhythmic clack of horse's hooves and turns to see her husband leading Master Osborn's horse, groomed and saddled from the stables. A voice from somewhere out of view floats up to her,

"He looks mighty fine today William!"

Her husband's reply is indistinguishable but he smiles with pleasure. She leans forward, pulls the curtain aside and peers down as the top of Master Osborn's hat comes into view. William slaps the horse's neck affectionately, the hollow sound reaching up to her window, then adjusts the stirrups and tightens the girth. Master Osborn mounts as William holds the chestnut hunter still, smiling up at the young man as if he hadn't a care in the world. She feels a spasm of anger. Why is it that men can only think of one thing at a time when women have a thousand things to remember, all carefully balanced to keep everyone healthy and happy? In different circumstances this thought would have made her smile and she would have articulated it at dinnertime along with some anecdote, after the men had gone back out to work. Now it just exasperates her. She scowls down at William standing with his hands on his hips watching Master Osborn ride off towards the village, then strolling back to the stables. Some men would have moved the dung heap there and then, as soon as the doctor mentioned it, even if it meant lighting a lantern to do it.

She sits back and quickly finishes off the stocking. The next job is Master Osborn's hunting coat. She rests the heavy material on her lap and investigates the tear where the sleeve joins the body of the jacket. The cloth is not damaged, having only been rent at the seam, but the fine inner lining is torn and will take longer. She pins the seam together and selects some heavy black thread and a strong needle. She would not have come today if it had not been for the doctor's visit last night, but his advice meant more expense and she could ill afford to lose her wages. She feels a rush of relief that she has kept up with the club subscriptions and was able to call the doctor as soon as Elizabeth was ill, without worrying about the cost. He had arrived with his greatcoat and hat dripping with rain and smelling of the night. Although not a tall man, his presence filled the cottage; the room seemed to shrink as he entered and the two older children retreated staring to the hearth.

Upstairs he had spoken kindly to Elizabeth and together they entreated her to open her mouth wide while the doctor held up his lantern and peered in, then put aside her clothing while he scrutinised the rash on her body. She complied but kept up her thin, high crying throughout, her eyes wide with fear despite Martha's reassurances and the doctor's gruff, "Good girl, good girl." His instructions to her had made her head spin. The other children were to sleep downstairs and were not to enter this room. Any rags used as handkerchiefs by Elizabeth were to be burnt, and her clothes placed in a bowl containing Condy's fluid. Martha had asked him to repeat this, which he had, and had told her where she might buy some. She was still repeating the instructions in her head as she saw him to the door.

"Have you a dung heap at the back door?" She had nodded, surprised.

"Have you a garden?"

"Oh yes sir, us has a good garden for taters."

"Then move the dung heap to the end of the garden, the malaria it gives off does not help in these cases of fever." He had put his hand kindly on her arm and his broad smooth face came close to her own thin, startled one.

"Do not be dismayed, your daughter is in no great danger. I shall call again on Friday to ensure that she is progressing well."

She remembers turning in relief to William and seeing the anxiety flood from his face and his hands shake as he reached to grasp the doctor's own. The memory of it makes her drop her sewing into her lap and she stares out at the tower with its mosaic of brown stone and the grey and silver sky beyond. He had felt the same as she had! She had not thought of it before, as the evening had been so full what with moving the beds downstairs and seeing to Elizabeth. He *had* helped her move the beds despite being tired after his walk to Bideford in the dark and the rain to fetch the doctor. She remembers too his hand reaching out to her in sympathy during the night when she returned to bed for what felt like the hundredth time. She had not reached back to him but had lain in tense, exhausted solitude, turned resolutely away from him and silently enumerating his omissions of feeling and lack of action. But of course he cared. Why had she not seen it before?

She turns back into the room and searches through a box of oddments until she finds a piece of green silk that is a close match to the lining of the coat. The trick is to cut it generously enough so that there is no strain on the new seams. She starts to cut and shape. It's strange, she thinks, how things change over the years, how you get used to things and forget to count your good fortune. Years ago she never dreamt she would be married with four children. When she reached thirty she was still single and had resigned herself to staying that way. No man had ever really shown interest in her or not the right sort of interest anyway. She knew why. Her hair was dark and straight and refused to curl whatever she did to it, and her face was thin and pale and she did not smile enough, she could not manage it somehow even when she felt quite happy. Men liked fair hair and curls and smiles and curves so that was that really. She had never thought of William *that* way; he was years younger than her, 11 years younger, and so shy that at first he would not look at her at all. He had come to look after the horses at the big house where she worked and she always made a point of wishing him a good morning, the same as she would for anyone, but it was several months before she got more than an embarrassed mumble in reply. However he always came in for his tea about the same time as she came down for hers and gradually they became friends, quite at ease in each other's company. She smiles to herself. It is a story she likes to go over in her head and would like to tell someone else, but all the people she knows are either family who know the story already and find it unremarkable, or are too busy to hear it. She suspects that if she did find someone to tell, it would not sound as interesting, so she prefers to tell it to an imaginary person in her head.

She remembers the day quite clearly. It was June and for a week the weather had been hot and sultry. Fourteen guests had been invited to a luncheon party by the master and mistress and the plan had been to hold it in the garden but today, though there was no decrease in temperature, clouds were building up in the south and the heat becoming heavy and threatening. The orders changed every few minutes, the party would be held in the dining room, - no, the sky was lightening and it would be held in the garden after all. The housemaids flitted from room to room with tablecloths and trays of glasses and the growing tension set everyone's nerves on edge. Martha had been called down to the kitchen to help and had been polishing glasses while William sat drinking his tea. He was unusually talkative, indeed he seemed unable either to stop talking or to look at her as he sat twisting his cup round and round in his hands. She had attributed his strange behaviour to the tense atmosphere in the kitchen and was beginning to feel irritated by his interminable story about a neighbouring gentleman's new horse when he exclaimed,

"Well, *I* shall act the gentleman now, - will 'ee walk out with me tomorrow?"

Martha smiles to herself as she remembers how in months and years to come, during rare moments of shared solitude then undreamed of, they had told each other their story and filled in forgotten details for each other. Laughing, he described the look of horror on her face at his suggestion. She protested that it was surprise, not horror,

"You could have knocked me down with a feather. I'd never had an urge to think of you that way."

"Well, you thought sewing more tempting than walking with me anyhow. 'Twasn't much of an excuse, was it!"

"'Twasn't sewing, 'twas washing, though I've never washed on a Sunday in my life. But I soon changed my mind, didn't I?"

Later, when the luncheon party - held in the dining room - was over, she had put a shawl over her head and gone out through the now heavy rain to the stables to find William with bowed head, cleaning a bridle. His face, when she had told him that she would walk with him after all, had been a delight to see, lit up just like his son's when, many years later, he had been given a long desired hoop and ash stick for Christmas.

After that the story gathered pace. They were already easy in each other's company and before long they were dawdling on the quieter footpaths together like any regular courting couple, though William had needed some encouragement to overcome his shyness. She had been surprised at her own boldness, the first time they had kissed. The memory makes her smile and her hands pause in their work as she stares at the wall next to her, picturing the scene. Not long after that they had agreed to marry and by the time spring came and the hedges were again starred with primroses and wild daffodils they were man and wife. Some difficult years followed; Mary and then William were born and they all lived in Barnstaple, but work was scarce and she took in washing for a while to help pay the rent. When William obtained the situation here in Littleham they lived apart for many months and visited rarely, the distance being too great for Sunday afternoon visits. Martha did some bits of sewing for a lady who lived nearby but the children had to be left with a neighbour and Mary, even then, was fretful and unhappy with anyone but her mother. Martha remembers returning to a cold, cheerless room with two tired babies and the neighbour's complaints ringing in her ears and crying with fatigue and loneliness.

When William did manage to visit her she found herself growing angry at his passive acceptance of their situation. He would tell her yet again that there were no houses to rent, but it seemed to her that he was making little effort to do anything about it. The more she chivvied him, the quieter and more withdrawn he became, which in turn drove her to greater heights of frustration and irritability in an effort to elicit a reaction from him. She remembers one occasion when she was haranguing him about their position shortly before he was due to leave. He sat staring at the floor then suddenly, without looking at her, rose and walked out of the door. She busied herself with washing and putting away the crockery, her movements agitated and impetuous as she silently enumerated and justified her frustrations. It was not until she heard the church clock strike four that she realised that he had indeed gone and she stared out of the dingy little window at the narrow rain-washed street, feeling she could never be happy again. Martha sighs, then, as the momentary sadness passes, returns to her sewing with renewed enthusiasm. The last part of the story is the part she most likes telling herself.

Their stilted little letters of apology crossed in the post, as did their next more effusive affirmations of love. Then another letter came from William, full of his usual equanimity, for nothing ever really roused him. There was a cottage to let in Littleham, a good substantial cottage with four rooms and a garden, and he had taken the "bold step" of agreeing to rent it. It would be theirs on Lady Day. She had arrived by cart with Mary and baby William and their few sticks of furniture to see William smiling at the top of the steps that led from the lane up to the little front garden, and they had walked from room to room together as she marvelled at the size and convenience of the cottage. She could not have thought more of it if it had been a palace. There was a good fireplace, a furnace in the scullery for washing, few signs of damp and a sunny sheltered garden with a good solid privy at the end. It was some distance to the well but they soon got used to that. The neighbours had been kind right from the start, wishing them happiness and bringing in little presents of a few potatoes or onions from their gardens, a bunch of flowers, even a rag rug from Maria Westcott. The Rector had given William a bed for the children and a little table. And now of course, it was even better for over the years they had whitewashed several times, cultivated the garden and made little improvements and, most importantly, it was home.

Martha knots and cuts the green thread and puts the jacket aside. The mending is finished now, but in a busy household there is always other work waiting to be done. She opens the deal blanket box where cloth and sheeting are kept and shakes some white cotton out on to the table. She searches through a drawer for the paper pattern she uses for aprons and smoothes this on top of the cotton. While she pins and cuts her thoughts are focused on the linen cupboard as she visualises and counts the aprons, caps and pillowcases, planning her Thursdays for the weeks to come. It gives her pleasure to have control over her work, to know what needs to be done without having to be told and to contribute to the smooth running of the household. It was one of the benefits of working in a smaller house without a housekeeper. She has never known the mistress of a household to be as painstaking or vigilant as a good housekeeper as they have too many other interests to distract them, and this suits Martha for she likes to be independent.

Settling by the window again and finding her thoughts drifting back to her own story and her imaginary audience, she takes up the narrative again.

"Us had been there two years near enough when Elizabeth was born and then Ellen two years after that. They'm good maids, all three, the first two quiet like their father and Ellen a proper toad and William's set to be a real little man and a good husband to someone one day. I never thought years ago to have such a family!"

She smiles as she pictures them all, herself included, walking back from church in their Sunday best, trying to see the family as others might. The girls all have their hair braided back from their faces with dark-coloured ribbons and would look like triplets were it not for their varying heights; everyone's clothes are tidy - though young William's socks are always down - and all six pairs of boots gleam with polishing. She and William walk arm in arm as the children dance around them and anyone can see that they are a good clean-living family. The children are always high-spirited after the long confinement in church and William is livelier than is usual for him, his face almost animated as he responds to the children's antics. She remembers too how his face lights up when he comes through the door in the evening and Ellen runs to him and how he always looks for her with his, "All right then my bird?" He is always composed; patient when Martha is irritable; a foil to her impetuosity. She leans forward and peers towards the stables, wanting the pictures in her head of his slow, patient ways and calm voice to melt into reality. There is no movement in the stable yard and her gaze cannot penetrate the squares of darkness above the lower doors. She regrets the irritation she felt towards him earlier. Men are different, that is all.

A movement from the opposite direction catches her eye and she turns to see Lucy Glover approaching the church gate with little Harriet skipping at her side. As they pass through the gate and Harriet in her comically determined manner closes it behind them despite being unable to reach the latch, Lucy looks up at Martha's window and waves. Martha drops her sewing in her chair and struggles to unfasten the window and lean out as Lucy shouts across to her.

"I've just see'd your Mary arrived back from Bideford. Her said to tell 'ee her's got that bottle for the doctor, her asked for it herself and there was no money to pay when they heard 'twas for the fever! Her said her'll go into town for 'ee any day now!"

"Well! - Her was as frighted as a rabbit earlier. Lucy, 'ave 'ee yurd news today?" Even from this distance Martha can see Lucy's usually radiant face cloud over.

"Two of the Piper children have it now, not the baby but the next two up and the older ones have gone off to school. Her says her wants them out from under her feet and 'tis best to catch it and be done with it."

Martha leans forward on the sill. "Well that idn't what the doctor said but then what can 'ee expect from 'er?" Their eyes meet in silent understanding.

Harriet appears round the side of the church, her bonnet askew, and runs to her mother, both hands clutched around a posy of snowdrops. "Mama, look what I finded!" Lucy smiles down indulgently at the little face glowing with satisfaction and straightens her daughter's bonnet. Harriet studies her treasure with the stillness of intense concentration.

"Where be 'ee gwain now then?" calls Martha.

Lucy lowers her voice a little. "Thought I'd take a look at

Sarah's resting place as the two little chiels are sleeping." She is silent for a moment. "Harriet's been saying when is Sarah gwain to come back from seeing Jesus and take Ellen home." Their gaze meets again across the clear cool air then Lucy waves and turns away.

Martha closes the window and returns to her seat. It is not over yet then. She feels a shiver of foreboding. Surely things cannot get worse? That is four cases of fever in the centre of the village where she lives. She imagines it expanding like a pall of smoke, but smoke which cannot be seen or smelled, which you only know you have inhaled when the pains and the rash start. She hopes Mrs Hockin will open the bottle of fluid straightaway for surely the smell of it will drive the fever away. She smiles with relief and pride as she remembers that Mary has returned safely with the bottle - and has not had to spend any money! All will be well now.

She works quickly along the bottom hem of the apron, the needle reliably picking up just two or three threads and producing tiny stitches of precisely uniform length despite her speed. She knots and cuts the thread, shakes and folds the apron, stands and stretches. It must be almost dinnertime. Perhaps by the time she has cut out another apron, the gong will sound. A movement outside attracts her attention and she glances out of the window, frowns in puzzled concentration. It is Mary, running, not for pleasure but with urgency, skidding through the side gate and down towards the back door of the Rectory. As she disappears from view Martha freezes, not knowing whether to go to the window or the door and her whole being shouting - it's Elizabeth! She must be worse, Elizabeth! Then in two strides she is out of the door and down to the first landing, leaning over the first banister to see Mary's flushed face looking up at her from below. For a moment they stare at each other, aghast, then Mary cries,

"Mother, come home, can 'ee come home? 'Tis Ellen, *her's* bad as well now."

# CHAPTER FOUR

The lane that leads from Littleham village to the church and rectory meanders between high hedge banks starred, on a warm May afternoon, with white stitchwort, red campion, blue germander speedwell and yellow buttercups interspersed with fresh new growth in shades of green so vibrant they seem to pulse with life. The hedges are alive with subdued squeaks and discreet rustlings that could originate either from small creatures or, seemingly, from the active, almost visible growth of vegetation. The lazy, repetitive call of a chiffchaff, so redolent of sunny spring days, is overwhelmed by a sudden rich burst of song, stopping as abruptly as it started, from a blackcap deep in the hedge ahead; a song thrush starts from its nest and waits watchfully on a nearby oak until I am safely distant. An orange tip butterfly celebrates with a leisurely, lilting waltz above the road before floating over the hedge to the field beyond; a speckled wood butterfly hesitates, quivering, on a low branch. It could be any year of the last five hundred or so, the only reminder that this is in fact the twenty-first century being the distant drone of a tractor cutting silage, and the tarmac road where the shadows of the hedgerow trees dance in the breeze.

The lane turns a little to reveal a more open scene of low banks and mature trees, shading the starry white flowers and luxuriant green leaves of wild garlic growing at their roots. The lane forks, winding down to the right past mighty trees and a small lake to the gracious, colonnaded Georgian rectory. I continue on the public road, which after a few yards widens and comes to an end in the small church car park. Ahead is the church, solid and indomitable as if forced up from the rock beneath by a geological fault in ancient times. To one side a small spinney is alive with the frenzied chirrups and wheezes of young birds demanding food. I know from previous explorations that amongst the trees are the barely discernible, ivy-covered remains of walls, the last traces of the poor house which was in use until the Bideford Union workhouse took over in 1836. On the right, adjacent to the churchyard is the back of the rectory, until a few years ago the less elegant side which originally housed the servants' quarters and rear yard. Now, in a strange reversal, the yard and new driveway are overlaid with cream and white gravel and the rear of the house renovated with the addition of an graceful Victorian-style conservatory running the length of the building; elegant potted palms now stand where the tradesmen used to call and the housemaids shake out their dusters.

A wrought iron gate leads from the car park into the churchyard, where the grass is left uncut around the older graves until the wild flowers have finished flowering; bluebells, early purple orchids and buttercups find shade among the long grasses from the warm sun. Above the ancient yew tree the sky is a brilliant turquoise against which swallows wheel and soar.

I pass out of the warmth into the church porch and push open the heavy oak door. As the latch clicks shut behind me the sounds of summer are cut off and the silence is complete. The church is cool and dark. Ahead a pedestal of white and yellow flowers gleams as if lit from within. As my eyes adjust to the gloom other colours appear: the gold leaf of the intricate rood screen; the sapphires, rubies and emeralds of the stained glass windows. A faint, musty odour is discernible and the air is strangely still.

On the back wall of the church a varnished wooden board is inscribed in gold lettering with the names of the rectors from earliest times to the present day. The first, "Date of Institution - Unknown", is "Sir Symon", the date of the second is 1337. I scan the list until I find the dates I want. 1843 - 1878, Joseph Lymebear Harding.

The rector had an important role to play in the nineteenth

century rural parish. He and his family had considerable social standing both for spiritual reasons and because they, along with the local squire's family, were often the only representatives of the educated upper classes. Being the only families educated to anything above a rudimentary standard, they were frequently in demand for advice on a wide range of matters and to write important letters for their parishioners. They were also valued as a source of work, for the "Big House" always employed numerous servants and it was an unfortunate village that lacked such an amenity on their doorsteps.

So what sort of man might Joseph Lymebear Harding have been? He would undoubtedly have been born into a privileged family and would have been well educated. He would not necessarily have had a strong calling to the church; throughout the nineteenth century it was the practice for the younger son of a wealthy family, who would never inherit his father's estate, to go into the church, for it was considered more respectable than commerce and less arduous than careers in law or medicine. This practice meant that some rectors were perfunctory in their duties and there were many instances of parishes that were left in the care of curates on miserably low pay, or parishes combined to increase income and only one of them tended. Some clergy spent far more time hunting than ministering to their parishioners, thinking nothing of cancelling all Sunday services on a regular basis in order to follow the hunt. Sabine Baring-Gould in his book of 1908, *"Devonshire Characters and Strange Events"*, claimed that earlier in the nineteenth century there were in the diocese of Exeter some twenty parsons who kept their own packs of hounds and over a hundred more who hunted two or three days a week. The most famous of these of course was Parson Jack Russell of Swimbridge who had both a breed of dog and a pub named after him and succeeded in being a popular priest as well as a sportsman. Others in coastal parishes became involved in smuggling and even wrecking or were, at least, not averse to having some contraband left on their doorsteps. However, many clergymen, of course, took their duties very seriously and took an active interest in village life in addition to their work in the church itself. It was not uncommon for the rector to organise educational provision, Sunday School outings and Christmas parties and to help with clothing, food and medication for those in need. He might also intervene with local landlords if he felt the cottages his parishioners inhabited were in need of renovation. Charles Kingsley was one of those to take his social duties very seriously.

The census was, of course, the easiest place to find information on the Reverend Joseph Harding. He was born in Arlington in North Devon but was brought up in Littleham, for his father was rector there from 1828 to 1843. By the time of the 1851 census, Joseph, aged 30, was named as the Rector and occupied the Rectory with his widowed mother and six live-in servants. Ten years later, in the 1861 census, his mother was no longer listed and Joseph Harding was married with four young children. The household consisted of Reverend Harding and his wife Maria, aged respectively 42 and 35, four children between the ages of two months and six years, and ten living-in servants; a housekeeper, housemaid, laundry maid, cook, kitchen maid, nurse, nursemaid, monthly nurse, footman and groom. These numbers were probably unusually high due to the very young age of the children; the monthly nurse would have been employed for a month after the birth of the baby. By the time of the next census in 1871, the year in which I was interested, only a cook, housemaid and parlour maid were living in. The circumstances were rather curious however; the Rector and his wife were away from home, "to London on business" as a footnote put it. The oldest son Osborn, then aged 16, was listed as head of household so he and his sister Josephine, aged 15, had to keep an eye on their two younger brothers of 11 and 10. It seems possible that other servants were employed but not living in.

Studying the census and other contemporary documents, one is able to build up a composite picture of a community through placing fragments of information like pieces of a jigsaw. Inevitably some pieces are missing and it is easy to make imaginative leaps to fill in the gaps, less easy to find the documentary evidence to prove the hypotheses. The Rector was away on April 4th, the time of the census. Throughout 1871 he officiated at only seven of 21 funerals and the majority of these seven were in the second half of the year, the rest were left to his curate. He did not officiate at any funerals at the height of the scarlet fever epidemic except that of George Reynolds, a gentleman "of independent means" living at High Park, who died from tuberculosis. Those are the facts, and it was tempting to flesh them out with conjecture. We know only that he was away from his parish on April 4th, but his absence may have been for much longer. Was it any accident that his stay coincided with the London Season, when wealthy families from all over the country converged on the capital for a social round of exhibitions, concerts, balls and sporting events? Certainly he was not the only one amongst the local gentry to be absent on census day 1871; from Moreton House in Bideford five males and seven females were "gone to London", at Portledge and Orleigh Court only servants were present and even Thomas Pynsent of Lakenham was away "visiting". I began to imagine that the Reverend Harding spent much time away from his parish, that he had little concern for the poor of his village but ensured he was available for his wealthier friends, but I was aware that I could be doing him an injustice. Historical research without the creativity to bring the facts to life can be a dull business, but in the interests of accuracy the facts must not be augmented without making it clear when reality ends and imagination takes over. How much easier it would have been if the Reverend Harding or his curate had kept a diary which by some lucky chance survived until the present day. They would have been the only ones likely to make a written record of the time, but no such document has appeared.

So what did Joseph Harding see when he stood in his church porch and looked out over the rolling hills of North

Devon? Did he see good hunting country and anticipate the thrill of the next chase? Perhaps he was more aware of the arduous, underpaid work of the labourers in the fields and sought for ways to improve their lives. Perhaps he was blind to social issues but rejoiced in the wonders of God's creation as he stood and stared, feeling the warmth of the sun on his shoulders through the heavy material of his long black coat. The green hills and wooded valley, the ancient church with its elegant rectory and spacious lawns, the copse loud with rooks. The contented, placidly chewing cows that plod and sway along winding lanes to the shippon on golden afternoons. It is a very English image and it exists still. How did he reconcile this privileged life with the sudden deaths of young children, the agony of loss of their parents? Could he stand up straight, look a mother in the eye when she asked the big question, the only question, - why? - and tell her that this was all part of God's plan? Perhaps he could. Or perhaps he turned his back on the cruel contrast and longed to be away from the narrow concerns of a small village, travelling on the railway from Bideford to Exeter and on to London to occupy himself with "business" – or pleasure. As he was away at the time of the census and officiated at few funerals, I began to think that the latter was most likely. There was other evidence; when he left Littleham in 1878 the new incumbent undertook extensive renovations of the church and the rectory, suggesting that they might have been neglected. No church school was built during his incumbency although this was a task undertaken by the rector in many villages; it was not until after the Education Act of 1876 that Littleham eventually formed a school board and built a school. None of these facts suggested that the rector was particularly diligent.

It was by chance that I found out a little more about him. Peter Christie, the energetic local historian, passed on to me any articles relating to Littleham that he found while pursuing his mammoth task of reading the *North Devon Journal* for the nineteenth century. I was able to find snippets of information about the Rector from these and from other local papers. The issue of 8th June 1865 carried a paragraph entitled "North Devon Archery."

"The first meeting of the session was held on Wednesday last on the beautiful grounds at Littleham, for many years devoted to the purpose by the Rev. Lymebear Harding. The meeting was well attended by the principal county families, and the weather most propitious. We saw, in regret, in the ladies a lukewarmness for the object of the meeting – archery, as a fashionable amusement, being in the ascendant. Croquet was played with energy, and dancing to Mr. Waldron's excellent band, kept up with spirit to a late hour. The pretty pavilion in which the dinner was laid was tastefully decorated with a profusion of ferns, flowers and flags, which (with the good order of the ground) showed that no pains had been spared by the hon. secretary to give his usual hospitable welcome to all-comers. This same pavilion has, we hear, been the means of giving pleasure and instruction to the people of Littleham, and the neighbouring parishes, for the last two years. Some excellent lectures, on divers subjects, and illustrated with dissolving views of as first-rate character, have been given by the Rector, evincing his desire in this, as in many other ways, 'to do good to all men'."

He seemed to be well thought of by "principal county families" but obviously also considered the well-being of his poorer parishioners. The "dissolving views" mentioned were magic lantern shows where by the use of a lantern with two or more lenses, or a pair of lanterns, two slides could be projected in such a way as to dissolve from one picture into another, producing effects such as day changing to night or summer into winter, special effects which must have seemed most startling and extraordinary to villagers who were only accustomed to the natural world.

I found another article that threw further light on the Reverend Harding's character, in the *Bideford Gazette* of 25th September 1877, some years after the period I was studying.

"LITTLEHAM
Harvest Thanksgiving Service. – Yesterday afternoon the

parishioners and friends of Littleham assembled on the Parsonage grounds, for the purpose of holding their annual harvest festival. In front of the Parsonage House, tables for tea were profusely spread for those who felt disposed to partake. A goodly number mustered, for the weather was as fine as most could wish, and to embrace the enjoyment, the worthy Rector threw open to the public his fernery and flower gardens. The youths indulged in the healthful game of football, whilst all the children, under fifteen years of age, belonging to the parish, were bountifully supplied with cake and tea. After which the visitors sat down and freely partook of the cup which cheers. The attendance was so great that one would think that all the parishioners present. Mrs. and Miss Harding did their best to please, and did it well. Bunting waved on the top of the old grey tower, and the bells sent forth their merry peals, and just before seven, the chimes called to the House of God, those assembled to enter in.... The preacher brought a profitable discourse to a close by placing before his hearers the claims of the Bideford Hospital. He showed the difficulty in cottage life of procuring for the sick the attendance they required. The Bideford Hospital was a place where all who were admitted received care and attention, combined with every comfort and cleanliness."

One wonders whether the scarlet fever epidemic of 1871 had any influence on his choice of charity.

During the nineteenth century, trade directories were published every few years for all counties. These were essentially forerunners of telephone directories and were aimed at commercial travellers. They gave descriptions of each town and village in the county together with a list of its churches, schools, inns and the names and addresses of its most noteworthy residents and its traders. I discovered that the Local Studies Library in Barnstaple held copies of all these directories and they proved to be a valuable source of information. *Kelly's Directory* for 1856 described Littleham as

"...a township and parish, two and a half miles southwest

from Bideford railway station, in Shebbear Hundred, Bideford Union, northern division of the county, Barnstaple arch deaconry and Exeter bishopric. The church of St. Swithin is an old stone building, in the early English style; repaired and the pews converted into open seats and otherwise beautified by the rector in 1847; has tower, nave, aisle, transept, porch, chancel, and 4 bells, monuments, font and stained glass windows. The living is a rectory, worth £202 yearly, with residence and 93 acres of glebe land, in the gift of Miss Antony and others. The Rev. Joseph Lymebear Harding, B.A., rural dean, is the incumbent. There is a school for boys and girls, principally supported by the rector. The population, in 1851, was 413. The soil in some parts is rich; the subsoil is clay. Miss Antony is lady of the manor, and, with Rev. J.L. Harding and Mrs. Anna Rolle Morrison, is the chief landowner. There are charities of 8s. yearly value. The parish is remarkably finely wooded, and the ground is very fertile. On the marshes skirting the stream of the Yeo, leading to Alwington and Parkham, there is a beautiful archery ground, where the North Devon Archers assemble during the summer months."

There followed a list of clergy and gentry, trades and professions, 29 people thought worthy of mention among a population of some 400.

*Billings' Directory* of 1857 wrote of the church as having

"...a fine painted window, placed there by the present Rector, through whose kindness and liberality this parish can boast of having one of the finest and handsomest interiors of any church in the county of Devon."

A Rector who took on the responsibility, and no doubt the financial burden, of renovating the church, who set up and supported a school from his own pocket, who had been considered worthy of the demanding post of rural dean, - that did not sound like someone who would choose to neglect his parishioners when they most needed him. Perhaps by 1871, at the age of 50, his energy and enthusiasm were beginning to wane somewhat.

He apparently retired when he left Littleham in 1878 at the age of 57 for when I traced him through the search facilities of the 1881 census CD-ROM he was described as a "Clerk in Holy Orders Without Cure of Souls". By a strange coincidence he was staying on the day of the census with one Charles Padley, Rector of Enville in Stafford. The same man had been staying at Littleham Rectory 30 years earlier during the 1851 census so they were perhaps close friends who had gone to theological college together. Joseph Harding was perhaps growing rather forgetful by this time as he gave his place of birth as Monkleigh, although it had been given as Arlington on two previous censuses. When we fill in our own census forms, it is intriguing to think how researchers may puzzle over any coincidences and idiosyncrasies in centuries to come.

While in Littleham, at least towards the end of his time there, he had the help of a curate. James Andrew was 47 years old in 1871 and lodged at Littleham Court with farmer William Heywood and his family. It must have been a strange and possibly rather lonely life, being associated both with the farmer's large family and the Rector's extensive household, yet an integral part of neither. His income would have been low and socially it is likely that he fitted neither into the higher social circles the Rector would have moved in, nor the close domesticity of village life. He did eventually achieve promotion; I found him listed in the 1881 census as Vicar of Hartington in Derbyshire, not far from his place of birth. He was still unmarried and shared the vicarage with a widowed housekeeper and a general servant.

In Littleham his work - and that of the Rector - must have been made more difficult by the strength of nonconformity in north-west Devon. By the mid-nineteenth century Methodism was stronger here than almost anywhere in England, with the notable exception of Cornwall; the 1851 census of religious worship recorded that 60% of worshippers were nonconformist. The Bible Christians, an offshoot of Methodism formed in Shebbear, had spread throughout the area with many small chapels being built in isolated agricultural areas; they had not, however, infiltrated Littleham, which remained staunchly Wesleyan Methodist. Since the eighteenth century the Church of England clergy had gradually become more closely affiliated with the gentry and had attained a higher standard of education; as a result their way of life had become remote from that of most of their parishioners. When the rector rode past on his horse or in his carriage, the labourer would stand aside and remove his hat; if he called at a cottage the flustered labourer's wife would address him as "Sir" and breathe a sigh of relief when he left. The Methodist preacher, by contrast, was usually of a similar social standing to his congregation and could understand their hardships and anxieties; he had little to do with the upper classes and was often a radical who raised awareness of social inequalities. He walked rather than rode to the service, which was often at a significant distance for the chapels were organised in local circuits with itinerant preachers. There was competition among his congregation as to whose turn it was to invite him to dinner afterwards.

The rector or curate with a dwindling congregation had, therefore, a difficult task and rivalry was strong. At times the division between Church of England clergy and Methodist ministers amounted almost to enmity. Neither church nor chapel were above using inducements to boost attendance, with Sunday School outings and Christmas treats high in the popularity stakes. In 1871 the *Bideford Gazette* carried a report on the Rector of Weare Giffard who expelled children from the Church of England school for attending a Wesleyan Band of Hope festival after he had refused to let them go. They had to pay to reregister at the school and he was criticised as a result. Rivalry seemed to be particularly strong where Church of England and Methodist schools existed within the same village; in this situation there were often instances of children being enticed to attend the rival school or minor skirmishes and name-calling between the two factions. It was not unusual for an employer to actively encourage his employees to attend a particular place of worship, and I found that the Littleham Church Register of Baptisms often contained the names both of farmers and the labourers they employed. Similarly the Bideford Circuit Wesleyan Register contained, for instance the Heywood family of Littleham Court farm and the Williams family who lived in the farm cottage. The curate James Andrew was indeed surrounded by nonconformists in his lodging there. It was on the subject of burials that there were frequent conflicts between Church and Chapel as, until 1880, Non-conformist ministers were not allowed to conduct funeral services in churchyards, a state of affairs that many found unacceptable.

I found no direct evidence of rivalry in Littleham and it is likely that life passed by peaceably most of the time - as of course it does today. Individuals and groups of people pass my house - and each other - on Sunday mornings, one set making for the church and the other for the chapel and there is certainly no antagonism; indeed in some cases members of the same household walk in different directions to their chosen places of worship. The only difference lies, perhaps, in the reduced numbers and in the presence of a larger group who continue past the chapel to reach the pub for Sunday lunch.

Littleham Methodist chapel was built in 1878. I was unable to find documentary evidence of the earlier chapel but had been told by a farmer born in 1900 that it had been located on the edge of the village next to a house now called Upadown and had been burnt down. It was not of course listed in the 1871 census as it had no inhabitants but there was a dwelling named as Chapel Cottage in that location, so his claim seemed to be justified.

Searching for the old chapel led me in turn on a quest to find the old school. The school that is still well remembered today was built in 1878 and closed in 1957. Although it was not until the 1870's that Education Acts, making school attendance compulsory, were passed, most towns and villages had some form of educational provision, and I already knew from the trade directories that the Reverend Harding had "supported" a school in Littleham. As with the chapel, the school was not listed in the census returns, nor was there any reference to a school on old maps, which suggested that there had not been a purpose-built building, and that the accommodation had perhaps been somewhat temporary in nature. The census returns did provide some clues, however, by giving the occupations of village inhabitants. Next to Chapel Cottage was Cooms Head, presumably the cottage now known as Coombe Cottage. The head of the household was named as Mary Sing, aged 65, a schoolmistress living with her daughter Sophia Bartlett, school assistant, and her husband Daniel Bartlett, a joiner. Could it be that Mary Sing held a dame school in her cottage? There were so-called dame schools throughout the country where children crowded into the living room of a cottage to receive a rudimentary education from a woman who was herself only a hesitant reader, in exchange for a few pennies. Another schoolmistress, Mrs. Susan Martin lived in Mount Pleasant. In *Morris's Directory* of 1870, she was named as the mistress at "a school for children of both sexes". In the 1871 census, there were 101 children in Littleham described as "scholars" and aged between three to four years and 13 to 14. Some 13 and 14 year olds and one 12 year old were in work. It seemed extraordinary that there were over a hundred children attending a school or schools which had left no clues or records of their whereabouts, so I set off again to the North Devon Record Office and Local Studies Library to see what I could discover. Here I found a copy of *'Early Devon Schools'* by Sellman, a writer who has spent many years researching the history of Devon schools, but although there were some clues, even he had failed to discover much information. He quoted the Parliamentary Returns of 1818, in which it was stated that there was no school in Littleham and the Rector of the time recommended,

"In the event of schools being established in country parishes, that the Parish Clerks should be appointed the schoolmaster by which means both offices might be better filled."

It would seem that remote villages were not popular with those sufficiently literate to carry out such duties. By 1833 however, Littleham was able to boast in the Parliamentary Returns of,

"2 day schools at parents' expense, 57 children in all. Church Sunday School - 30 children, Methodist ditto. 46 children, both supported by contributions. All schools established since 1818."

Obviously great developments had been made in the intervening 15 years but I was unable to find such detailed information about later years. The only references to schools in Littleham were in the trade directories, all of which mentioned only one school, sometimes with a reference to it being supported by the Rector. It may be, of course, that the Rector himself supplied the information, in which case he might have omitted to mention a Methodist or dame school. Records of schools are more likely to have survived when the school in question was receiving a government grant. National and British schools, supported by charities affiliated to the Church of England and Nonconformity respectively, received grants and later these were extended to other schools, but all wishing to receive a grant had to be willing to be inspected regularly by government inspectors. These were feared as much as Ofsted inspections are today, perhaps more so as, later in the century at least, teachers' pay could be cut if the children did not achieve a satisfactory standard. It was not surprising if some schools, and it would seem that Littleham was one of them, chose to remain independent and rely on donations and the pennies sent by parents.

Another book in the Library, Bovett's 'Historical Notes on Devon Schools', mentioned Littleham but only to state that there was no record of where the school had been and that it might have been held in the Rectory.

As I walked around Littleham, the village of 1871 had become as real to me as the village of the present. I could picture cottages which had long since disappeared; small, red, horned cattle standing patiently in farmyards before milking; children playing on dusty roads devoid of traffic; a woman in long skirt and apron, about whom I knew more than I did of many of my present day neighbours, hanging out her washing. In this village up to a hundred children had walked to a school or schools every day, a place that would have been central to village life, yet I did not know where it had been. Even now as I write, I look at my watch and seeing that it is almost four o'clock instinctively look to the window. Surely if I half close my eyes I shall be able to see the children passing in twos and threes, laughing and pushing each other, glancing up at my window and waving? Perhaps tomorrow morning I can follow them and see where they go, for sometimes this seems a more reliable way of finding the school than consulting books and documents.

Perhaps a school *was* held in the Rectory, or in the old poor house alongside. Pamela Horn, in her book *"The Victorian Country Child"* gave examples of schools being held in a vicarage kitchen and scullery, a vicar's loft, a stable in the vicarage garden and in the north aisle of a chapel. Dame schools were also common throughout the country. It certainly seems possible that the two schools that existed in 1833 remained in existence a lot later than the entries in the trade directories suggested. There would seem to be little reason to close a chapel school when there were a hundred children to be educated, a majority of them Methodist. Perhaps the difficulty in amalgamating two disparate schools caused the delay in building new premises; certainly when a school board was eventually formed in 1875 it included at least one farmer who was Methodist, in addition to the Reverend Harding, which suggested some sort of compromise.

Although all the children in Littleham were described in the census as "scholars", it is likely that school attendance fell far below what would be acceptable today. Until, and indeed for some time after, the Education Act of 1880, when full time attendance at school was made compulsory for children between five and ten years of age and part time attendance for those between ten and fourteen, many children went to school only sporadically. In rural areas most were employed at least part time. There were many seasonal activities that could be performed by children, a situation which suited both the farmer, who saved on adult wages, and the parent for whom any extra income could make the difference between being able to pay the bills and going hungry. Many, therefore, only went to school when work was not available, otherwise spending their time stone-picking, bird-scaring, weeding, haymaking, harvesting and fruit picking. Girls were very often kept at home to care for younger brothers and sisters, to help their mothers with domestic chores or to carry out paid work in the home such as glove making, a craft that was widespread in North Devon. It was not uncommon for parents to see little point in their children attending school when they themselves could not read and many employers were firmly opposed to education, believing it would give their employees "ideas above their station" and preferring a passive workforce. Even for those parents who were willing for their children to go to school, there were further problems such as the difficulty in affording the penny or two a week in school fees and the cost of boots of sufficient quality to withstand a wet walk to school. A new pair of child's boots could cost 14 shillings, the equivalent of a week's wages for a labourer, so it is easy to see how problematic footwear could be for a family with seven or eight children. In some households children took it in turns to attend school wearing whatever boots were available, irrespective of their size, and the remaining children remained at home barefoot.

Those who did manage to attend school received an education that was rudimentary to say the least. The majority of teachers were untrained and some, particularly those running dame schools, had attained only basic standards of literacy. Mary Sing and her daughter, the schoolmistresses living at Cooms Head in Littleham, had been working as gloveresses in 1861, a menial and low-paid occupation that certainly did not suggest a high standard of education. Earlier in the century it was common for nothing but reading to be taught, and no books except the Bible to be available. Even when a greater range of reading matter was brought in, it was hardly inspiring. According to Pamela Horn in "*The Victorian Country Child*"

"The reading books chosen were often either very boring or extremely sad and gloomy in content, and sometimes both. It was scarcely surprising if the children's minds wandered as they read or chanted such phrases as:
'The gold of a guinea might be drawn out so as to reach nine miles and a half. This property in gold of being capable of extension to so extraordinary degree is owing to its great tenacity or cohesion of particles.' "

Other reading primers contained lessons using only two letter words for children who had just learnt the alphabet, and contained such nonsensical rhymes as,

"As we do, so do ye,
Be to us, as we to ye,
C is as we go by,
Do ye go to it, or no. "

Rote learning rather than understanding was usual. Children learned to copy dull repetitious phrases on to slates, to chant rhymes and numbers in unison for long periods of time and to recite the Church Catechism. It is hardly surprising that they struggled when the time came to do arithmetic for only then were they required to think. When inspectors carried out examinations in the three 'Rs', it was inevitably in arithmetic that the children achieved the lowest results, as an inspector quoted in Sellman's *'Devon Village Schools in the Nineteenth Century'* confirmed:

"Examined Third Standard in Arithmetic: they are a slow lot. It was a mistake for them to be born in an age of steam."

The only other subject to be generally taught was needlework for the girls, thought to be essential as they would have to make and mend all their family's clothes when older.

121

If the subjects taught were dull, the school day was not made any easier for pupils or teachers by the conditions in which they had to work. It has already been seen that buildings were often makeshift; in addition they were frequently extremely cold in winter and there are many reports in school logbooks of children having to cease writing because their fingers were too cold to hold a pencil. Classes were often very large and there are records of seventy children of all ages being taught by one teacher and a twelve-year-old monitor; numbers such as these would have been unusual but many teachers had to cope with up to 40 children of all ages in one room. The youngest were only three and sometimes even two years old. Although the presence of these younger children in the classroom made the teacher's job extremely difficult - playthings in school were unheard of at that time - many teachers were reluctant to refuse them as if they did so, their older siblings would also remain at home to look after them with a consequent loss of school fees.

It seems that unless some previously unnoticed documents are found, the whereabouts of the old Littleham schools will never be known. The existence even of the later school, which finally closed in 1958, is unknown today to many newcomers in the village. After its closure it was used for many years to house chickens, the boarded-up windows and wind-blown drifts of straw threatening the solid Victorian stone walls with dereliction. Perhaps at that stage it could still, with the aid of a more enlightened education authority, have been reopened, but it was sold and converted to a dwelling. Flowers and a lawn now grow where generations of children played and shouted, and the village is empty of children until the cars and school taxis return with them at four o'clock.

Wherever the school or schools were in Littleham in 1871, the numbers on school roll would have been sadly depleted early in the year. Any children with brothers and sisters suffering from scarlet fever would have been asked to stay at home in an effort to stop the spread of the disease, but it is also likely that the school would have closed altogether for a time. The figures I had obtained were, after all, only of those who had died; many more children would have contracted scarlet fever and recovered, and it is likely that in a small community where so many families were interrelated few if any households escaped the disease altogether. It would have been a devastating time, not only for the families involved but also those in positions of authority, the teachers and clergy.

# *The diary of James H. Andrew,*

## *Curate of Littleham.*

<u>Friday 20th January 1871.</u>

A fine, dry day with a light south-westerly breeze. As I rode from my dwelling I happened to notice the first primrose of this year which caused me to muse on the comparatively short duration of the winter season. Even during the darkest days God sends us messages of hope, a theme that might well prove comforting in Sunday's sermon.

Upon my arrival at the Rectory I found the yard strangely quiet and even a loud "hulloa there" brought forth no response so I was forced to stable my horse myself. One of the servants then appeared to inform me that William Powe's children have the scarlet fever; I was saddened by the news, as he is a sober, steady man. In the schoolroom I found the number of children to be diminished through the fever and I was hard-pressed to obtain answers to my questions. To stare and to cough they were able but to answer the simplest questions on my chosen text they most certainly were not able. The slowness of the Devon character when compared with that of my native Lancashire is something to which I fear I will never become accustomed. Mrs Martin encouraged and prompted them and if it had not been for her presence, I fear my anger would have risen. I have asked that she read them the text again, that I may obtain more satisfactory answers on Monday.

Upon leaving the Rectory, I paid a call on Mr and Mrs Dennis and we prayed together for Sarah's soul. Mrs Dennis finds this most comforting and thanked me kindly for remembering her. I obtained little response from her husband however, he seems quite brought to his knees by their sad loss. As I untethered my horse I could hear the ringing of the anvil in the smithy and could just detect young George Glover working in the gloom as the furnace flashed red and the sparks flew. His master is doing little work as yet and it seems he has become a valuable worker.

It being such a fine day, I thought to take a walk after luncheon and descended again to the village, which was strangely quiet but for numerous speckled fowls on the village street and labourers at work in adjacent fields. I continued down through the steep and narrow ways towards the Bradworthy road. The prospect from here is one seldom succeeded in beauty or distinction; the fields and wooded hills dropping to the wide and fruitful vale intercepted by the meanders of the gleaming River Yeo; all unite to proclaim the goodness of God in the provision he makes for his flock. Once in the valley, I paused on the bridge that crosses the river adjacent to Kingdom's Mill, startling a grey heron, which lifted its great wings and flew ponderously downstream towards the confluence with the Torridge.

I was served with a fine piece of beef and potatoes for dinner.

<u>Saturday 21st January 1871.</u>

I was awakened at a very early hour by the shrill tones of Mrs Heywood rising from the yard beneath my window as she directed the loading of the market cart with panniers of eggs and vegetables. I was forced to recall my first days at Littleham Court when I wondered at God's purpose in choosing for me to be installed above a farmyard and amongst such a hubbub of people and animals, fearing that I should be too weary from want of sleep to carry out His work. Today I was thankful that I was able to sleep once again after the cart had departed with much rattling and creaking for Bideford.

When Eliza brought my breakfast, she informed me that the condition of Elizabeth, the seven-year-old daughter of Mr and Mrs Powe, had worsened and I resolved to call on them at the earliest opportunity. I then spent a quiet morning preparing my sermon and am sufficiently pleased with it.

I saddled my horse myself and as I rode to the village overtook quite a party returning with their purchases from Bideford, being three families who had joined together for the company on their homeward journey. Their numbers, together with the children who played as they travelled, were sufficient to quite fill the road. Their spirits were high and so immersed were they in their stories and their mirth that they barely noticed my presence and I could still hear their laughter ringing from the hillside some minutes later after I had turned the corner at the crossways. The enjoyment and support the cottagers find in each other's company must be a great comfort to them.

On arriving at the Powe's dwelling in Mount Pleasant, I was greeted by a small knot of women who were gathered at the gate, talking together and comforting one another. I recognised one to be Mrs Westcott, the cottager with an idiot child. Their voices died away as I arrived, but then one gathered her wits and said,

"Her's gone, zur, poor little maid's passed away."

I tethered Bruno in the road and with some trepidation knocked at the door. After a pause it was answered by Mr William Powe. I recited the words of sympathy I had rapidly rehearsed and he thanked me kindly although appearing rather stupefied, poor man. He asked me into a small room sparsely furnished with a deal table, three or four hard chairs, a cupboard and a shelf containing a few trinkets. A great pot and a kettle stood on the hearth. We proceeded up the narrow staircase where I had to stoop considerably to avoid knocking my head. We found his wife in a small bedroom sitting with the two remaining daughters who, it transpired, were also recently struck down with the fever though only the youngest with any severity. We repaired to the second bedroom where the body of Elizabeth lay, an affecting sight when she was so lately full of life and vigour. A woman, a relative no doubt, kept watch at her side. We prayed together at her bedside but Mrs Powe seemed quite unable to join in the responses, clung to her husband staring first at the child then at me in a manner which quite unsettled me and I hardly knew whether I should continue. Suddenly she cried out,

"Pray for *them,* pray for the other poor chiels, 'tis too late for poor Lizzie!"

I confess I was shocked at her lack of concern for her daughter's soul but included some prayers nevertheless that the Lord save her remaining children should He see fit.

Mr Powe saw me to the door and his son William also came to greet me. It seemed that while the mother was nursing the dying child upstairs the two of them had worked into the night by lantern light moving the dung heap, shovel-load by shovel-load, to the far end of the garden, on the instructions of the doctor. They had believed that in doing so, the course of the disease would be halted, a vain hope I fear. Both father and son appeared quite knocked up from overwork and lack of sleep.

Roast pheasant tonight, a dish I find most enjoyable.

Sunday 22nd January 1871.

A day of strong winds and intermittent heavy rain. The congregation was small, which I assumed to be on account of the weather, churchgoing being but a fickle affair for many hereabouts. After the service I found Mr Edward Morrish and Mr John Bale, who are chapel-goers, waiting outside the church for me and they conversed at length with me. It seems I have underestimated the severity of the fever. As their farms are both situated centrally in the village they are aware of the latest developments and, informing me that there have been more cases in the last two days, demanded to know what action I intended to take. I assured them that in the event of a death, the funeral would take place as quickly as could be arranged to avoid the risk of further infection. I confess I felt at a loss to know what else was expected of me. It is at such times that I feel most keenly the absence of the Reverend

Harding and the valuable advice he would no doubt offer. I have resolved to write to him and inform him of the situation. Mr Morrish gave his opinion that both schools should be closed to limit the spread of the infection. I have decided that this should be done and will suggest to Mrs Martin tomorrow that she give the children a day's notice, closing after the afternoon session on Tuesday. The other school is not, of course, my concern.

My sermon was, I think, well received despite the limited numbers. There were two or three women present who attend irregularly and had, I believe, come to pray for those close to them who are sick and they, in particular, seemed to derive some comfort from my words. Today was also the happy occasion of the baptism of Mr Barry's baby daughter, a surprisingly solid little child for her very young age. As I was about to anoint her, she suddenly adjusted her gaze so that she could see my face, stared in a most determined manner at me then gave a smile akin to the sun emerging from dark clouds, causing me to stumble over my words. I confess I was quite taken with her and experienced some reluctance when the time came to hand her back to her mother.

Monday 23rd January 1871.

A dull day with no hint of brightness. As I stood at my window after breakfast, I saw little Ann Williams from the farm cottage, an angular, bony child, struggling to carry a large tub of water from the pump. Later she was at the mangle with two babies rolling in the mud at her feet. I have rarely seen the mother since the child died before Christmas and I hear that she sits indoors staring at the walls in a state of melancholy. I have not visited for I fear I would not be welcome but I have seen Mr Allen, the Methodist minister, calling on two or three occasions. Ann, though only a child herself, has developed the stooped, worn-out look that so many of the village women display.

The funeral of Elizabeth Powe was at two o'clock and it was a sad little procession that led from her cottage to the church as the bell tolled. The sight of a small coffin is always affecting and in this case it was followed only by her father and two elderly relatives. Mrs Powe, quite broken down, remained at home to care for the other children, all of whom are now stricken with the fever. The church was, of course, full almost to capacity.

I have rarely seen a father in so wretched and unmanned a condition as was William Powe and I almost dreaded approaching him after the little coffin had been laid in its resting-place. My words, though carefully chosen, seemed to hold little comfort for him. I assured him that Elizabeth was safe and at rest with the Lord in the Eternal City. He looked up at me and weeping openly as he spoke, said in that thickened accent, which I still struggle to understand,

"Zur, 'tis only her grandfeyther as has gone before and her won't know 'un, it being four years since 'a passed on. There be no other to care for her and her'll be all alone in that girt place, poor li'l chiel."

If it had not been for the man's obvious distress, I fear I should have smiled but I conquered this desire and reminded him of Psalm 31.

A plate of ham for dinner. Mrs Heywood engaged me in conversation, or harangued me rather, for longer then I would have wished. She believes that the fever would be contained if the recommendations as to the sanitary measures were heeded but I fear this is impossible in overcrowded cottages. The conditions present in some of the worst cottages are intolerable. I shall perhaps intimate to the Reverend Harding on his return that he should again challenge the most culpable landlords. It has been proved in other localities that spacious, sanitary cottages can be built without incurring too great an expense. This is a subject that interests me a great deal.

Tuesday 24th January 1871.

A cold day, and a cold breakfast, as is usual on market days. I knelt and prayed for longer than is my wont. My weaknesses and fears were foremost in my reflections. I had thought to walk in the hills to a place of beauty and tranquillity that I have found to be well suited to solitary meditation. However the Lord helped me to confront my fearfulness and to realise that I must do those things which are part of my duties here, however hard I might find them. I prayed that He might help me find the words that bring peace and acceptance to others, that I might not be overcome with silence, and I set off to visit the afflicted households.

I went first to the school; having noticed on passing that the other school has already closed. I spoke to Mrs Martin who assured me that after today the children would not return until the fever has abated. Indeed there were few present today. I spoke to those that remained, entreating them to serve their parents well and to remember their lessons, and their mournful little voices chanted their accordance.

Returning to the village, I called first at old Mrs Hookaway's shop, being more certain of my reception there. I accepted the offer of a cup of tea and we withdrew to the back room and the company of Miss Brooks who nodded and smiled, a picture of acquiescence, while we conversed. Mrs Hookaway is a charming, bright-eyed old lady who despite a life of undoubted hardships, speaks well of everyone and has a generosity of spirit that many would do well to emulate. She spoke of other epidemics she has seen in her long life;

"'Tis a gift from God, zur, that He chooses some to fly to Him, but 'tis grievous hard for the parents to let 'em go."

Taking my leave with my spirits somewhat higher, I called next at Mr William Piper's dwelling, being the large cottage second from the end in Mount Pleasant. He was of course at work on the farm and my knock was answered by his daughter Sarah, a tall, bold-looking girl of twenty years or thereabouts, who seems quite devoid of any female graces. She demanded what she could do to help me in a manner which was almost churlish and when I explained - my confidence fast waning - that I had come to enquire after the health of her brothers and sisters and to offer my prayers, she declared that I had better enter. I found myself in a shabby

131

room, the floor damp throughout and even muddy near the door, no bright furnishings to lighten the gloom, and a potato sack thrown down in place of a rug before the hearth, where burnt a meagre fire. A baby crawled on the floor and, seeing me, pushed itself into a seated position and stared up at me, its face smeared with dirt. A small boy lay sleeping on a straw mattress.

"'E sleeps down yur" she told me "so as to be away from the maids, but 'e's caught'n anyways. Only boy 'mongst twelve of us, see, and us have only lost three, through the years. You can go up, if 'ee want to pray for 'em."

And with that she sat in the window seat and picked up the glove she was sewing. I hardly knew whether to protest at such a rude reception but being, as so often, sadly lost for words, I turned to climb the stairs, thinking that the Reverend Harding would not be spoken to in such a manner. I found myself in a low room, bare but sufficiently clean, and could just make out a low straw bed by the little light that seeped in the one small window, its frame patched with rags. Two small girls lying in the bed shrunk away from me, their eyes wide with surprise. I asked their names and enquired as to their state of health but could on no account elicit a response. I knelt and said the Lord's Prayer but they continued to stare in silence, and as I turned back down the stairs, I heard one starting to weep.

Their sister had little to say when I had descended and it was with considerable relief that I closed the cottage door behind me. The girl has such a brazen look that I fear she may go the way of her father's three sisters, who between them have peopled the area with baseborn children.

Outside I took a deep breath, whispered a prayer and turned to the Powe's cottage next door. At the gate I met with Mrs Westcott on her way out who clasped my hand and with tears in her eyes told me it was "turrible, zur, turrible," so it was with considerable trepidation that I knocked at the door. William Powe, looking most unwell, seemed relieved to see me and urged me indoors. The cottage bore a strong odour of disinfectant and it was with many apologies that I was asked to rinse my hands in a bowl of the said liquid at the top of the stairs. Mrs Powe came to me and thanked me effusively for coming; she appeared restless in the extreme and her eyes were bright and feverish with distress. The two older children lay in separate beds, their faces flushed. The boy slept. Both had had their heads shaved in an attempt to prevent further infection and I was dismayed at their unnatural and unprepossessing appearance. The window was open, having apparently been ordered so by the doctor, but Mrs Powe confided in frightened tones that she would soon have no dry blankets to keep the children warm, due to the necessity of soaking so many in disinfectant. I promised to acquire some for her, then, in response to her pleading, knelt to pray for the children. The girl, Mary, joined in with some of the responses and whispered a request that we should say a prayer for her sister Ellen, who lay in the next room. We then passed into the second room, the very one where Elizabeth's body had lain. We found little Ellen in a grievous state, burning with fever and trembling all over, her eyes wide open yet unseeing, her breath coming fast and shallow. I confess I was shocked and I prayed long and most fervently that God's will be done, while the afflicted parents wept.

Mr Powe accompanied me downstairs. He told me how their neighbours were being most helpful, bringing food ready prepared though he and his wife could eat but little, and keeping the fire alight and the room clean. The doctor called each day and his advice was followed to the letter. I asked him whether there was any other way in which I might help.

"Just pray, zur, 'tis all us can do now, zur, pray."

I urged him to look to his own health, for he had a flushed, besotted appearance not unlike that of his children, and departed.

I have not the heart to write in detail of my other visits. Suffice to say I called on Mrs Mary Vilot at East Furlong Cottages, as miserable a dwelling as one could find anywhere in the country; the family of Mr Thomas Mitchell at Lower

Langdon Cottages which consists of four babies all under five years of age, and Widow Hern at Moorhead whose daughter has the fever. None were in quite such a bad way as little Ellen Powe and, perhaps as a consequence though it pains me to entertain such a thought, nowhere were my prayers quite so well received. I left each house feeling I had been unable to find words of sufficient consolation and had brought very little comfort. There was more interest in my offers of material help such as blankets and disinfectant, which I shall purchase with the Alms. Though I would not declare it in public, it sometimes seems to me to be as difficult for a poor man to enter heaven as a rich; the rich man's head is full with thoughts of the goods he possesses and the poor man's with thoughts of those things he lacks.

I wrote to the Reverend Harding this evening and informed him of the worsening situation. Also to my dear mother from whom I received a letter this morning.

Wednesday 25th January 1871.

The news has just come to me, now after dinner, that little Ellen Powe has died at the tender age of five years. This news fills me with sadness. Will this dreadful fever take yet more young lives? If that is God's will, then so be it. May He have mercy upon her soul and may her parents find comfort in His love. I have sent a message that her funeral shall be at 11 o'clock tomorrow.

This morning after breakfast I sat and read for some little while. I found 2 Corinthians, chapter 4 most comforting. However discouraging the circumstances I must be unstinting in my duties and continually remind my parishioners of the power of prayer. I am aware of the modern trend for the clergy to be all things to all men and to be involved in many affairs that have no direct bearing on the Church; to be actively engaged in matters of education, agricultural theory, social policy and housing. There are some that seem able to balance this role with a life devoted to the Church and to prayer; the Reverend Harding is one. Others seem to me to neglect the spiritual life when they take on the social concerns of their parishioners. I am an instrument in the hands of God and His word, spoken by me, can bring the love and fear of God to the hearts of others. My role as provider of alms is but secondary.

The day was dry and bright so I pulled on my boots and strode out, feeling much in need of air after yesterday's close confinement with the sick in dark cottages. My spirits rose and I took pleasure in the view from the steep descent of Moorhead Hill across the wide valley below and over to the facing hills. Meandering hedgerows and patches of woodland partitioned the land into enclosures of every shape and size, in many hues of green and brown. The lofty tower of Buckland Brewer church reached up from the skyline and behind it grey and silver clouds drifting from the south west piled up on the horizon, and above was an infinity of blue. Halfway down the hill I leant on a gate and watched as a carriage pulled by two trotting horses proceeded steadily up the hill on the other side of the valley towards Buckland Brewer; the rhythmic clatter of their hooves was carried to me on the breeze while a nearby roadside streamlet provided a tinkling counterpoint. In the field before me a labourer clearing a ditch straightened, stretched and, perceiving me, raised his cap in greeting. A pair of buzzards rode the wind on outstretched wings, gliding, turning and rising with never a wing beat, meeting and almost touching only to glide apart again, their high-pitched mewing cries all the while belying their great size. These were precious moments when I felt close to the Lord yet still I pondered on His aims for me. Unlike the labourer in the field I am unsure of my specific place and purpose in society. Is His purpose for me to bring the knowledge and love of God into people's homes or to teach me greater humility and awareness of my own worthlessness? If it is the former I know I am not yet achieving His purpose for I so often remain silent in company, unable to find the words that would be most valued.

I had thought to walk through the woods to the Rectory but

as this would have meant returning through the centre of the village and the likelihood of further meetings, I took the earlier turning. As I turned a corner on the hill I saw two figures in a close embrace in the shadow of the high bank below Higher Langdon. On hearing me, they broke hurriedly apart, she scurrying up the road to disappear up the track to Higher Langdon and he, for it was young George Glover, forced to walk towards me to return to his work at the forge. I affected to have noticed nothing untoward and wished him a civil good morning, to which he replied with averted face. Should I perhaps have warned him of the dangers of debauchery? He has good prospects at the forge and I would not like to see him jeopardise his future. On my way home I pondered on what I might have said, a difficult subject indeed to address.

More reading tonight, and a dinner of boiled beef with cabbage and potato.

### Thursday 26th January 1871.

It was with a heavy heart that I set off this morning for the funeral of Ellen Powe. I reached their cottage in Mount Pleasant in good time in order to say some prayers with the grieving parents and found their neighbours already gathering, to walk as one to the church. The mood was sombre indeed. Inside I found Mrs Powe ready to attend her daughter's funeral, old Mrs Hookaway sitting upstairs with the other children. The mother appeared benumbed, sitting with bowed head and seemingly unheeding of my words; it was for her husband that I had more immediate concerns for he cried out and wept in anger rather than sorrow, demanding to know what grievous sins he might have committed to be punished so. I prayed aloud and most fervently that he might benefit from his affliction by learning submission to God's will and learn to see his children's deaths as a providential dispensation. I trust that God in His infinite wisdom will enable him to reach acquiescence in the fullness of time. He carried the coffin himself with his wife at his side and two relatives behind; his sobs were unceasing as I walked before them. I confess I found it arduous to pronounce the words of the service again, just three days after the first and it was particularly poignant to see the little coffin placed in the grave next to that of the older sister.

When I returned home it was in a strange and disturbed frame of mind. Despite the parents' great sorrow they have the consolations of their remaining children, of each other, of the love and unending support of their community who, I knew, would now be gathering around them. I paced my cold and empty rooms and I confess there was envy in my heart for they, at least, have known love. May God forgive me such thoughts.

Friday 27th January 1871.

Mrs Heywood brought my breakfast this morning along with a letter from the Reverend Harding, which I opened with some eagerness. It was brief but brought the welcome tidings that he will be returning tomorrow for a few days and cordially invited me to join him and his family for dinner tomorrow evening. It was apparent that my letter had not yet reached him but it seemed that he had had news of the progress of the fever from other sources, for he referred to recent events. I look forward with anticipation to his thoughts on the matter.

Mrs Heywood was today given, in return for a favour, a splendid salmon netted in the Torridge. She served me a portion tonight and it was very fine indeed.

Saturday 28th January 1871.

I spent much of the day reading sermons, the weather not being favourable for going about. I asked for my horse to be saddled at five o'clock as the Reverend Harding had asked that I might attend early, that he and I might converse before dinner. The village was deserted as I rode through, and dark but for the gleam of candles in cottage windows. I observed that in the first cottage in Mount Pleasant, that of the Powe family, the lower windows were in darkness but a light shone from one upper window. I have had no tidings today as to the progress of the two remaining children.

I rode to the front door where my horse was taken by a man who was a stranger to me and it transpired that he has come over from Monkleigh to take care of the horses and wait at table during William Powe's absence. I was told that the poor fellow has taken to his bed now. I was shown to the Reverend's study where he greeted me warmly; I confess I was extremely pleased both to see him and indeed to be in company again. Once talking to him many of my anxieties appeared groundless for he seems to find a simple and eminently sensible solution to all problems. He was saddened to hear my account of the course of the fever and particularly my account of the deaths of William Powe's daughters. He suggested that we should visit the afflicted households together tomorrow afternoon, a proposal which cheered me greatly as I was aware that my further visits were somewhat overdue.

He has many practical and useful suggestions, which I feel I should have conceived for myself. He asked whether I had met with Dr Ackland and when I confessed I had not, stated that we should do so together, in order that the doctor's recommendations might be reinforced to the parishioners. He has himself read widely on the subject of fevers and emphasised that the most effective precaution was to prevent the initial infection by limiting contact as far as possible. He recommended that I should no longer visit a sick child's bedside but limit my contact to the parents except when death is imminent, and ensure that well-wishers do the same. He also felt that the time has come to limit mourners at funerals to those who are of the immediate family. This is a measure which will be taken very hard for the cottagers will feel they are not supporting the bereaved family if they stay away, but I can see that it is necessary to prevent the spread of the infection. Of course it may be that none of these measures will be put into practice, for it is quite probable that the fever has now run its course.

The Reverend Harding was also most kind and reassuring about my spiritual care of the parishioners. I was greatly encouraged by the time our meeting came to an end and we were called in to dinner.

It was altogether a most pleasant and convivial evening and a most satisfying dinner of turbot and saddle of mutton. The table was attractively set and as I gazed around at the gleam of candlelight on silverware and the answering shine in dancing eyes, I could not but contrast the scene with my habitual lonely table. All four children stayed up for dinner, the two younger boys now being of sufficient age to join Osborn and Miss Josephine and to provide amusing and lively company. I sat opposite Miss Josephine who in recent months has become a young lady of considerable poise and charm. The conversation ranged across diverse subjects and I fear the claret loosened my tongue somewhat. My comments appeared to be well received however. We retired to the drawing room for preserved fruits and more conversation and it was late when I left.

Sitting now in my chair back at Littleham Court after a moonlit ride through the silent village, the cottages huddling together in shadowy companionship, I feel in a better frame of mind than I have for some weeks. If there is good in me which can be put to use, Lord, it is Thine to use as You see fit.

Sunday 29th January 1871.

I performed the service and administered the sacrament this morning as arranged, so that the Reverend Harding can spend more time with his family for his time here is regrettably brief. There were again many parishioners present and I was inclined to wonder whether it is wise for a large number of people to gather and possibly spread infection, yet the need for prayer and for the support of the community of the Church is strong at this time. There are indeed difficult decisions to be made.

Another baptism this week, Julia Ann, yet another

baseborn child of Mary Piper. She has had five over the years of which I am aware, which perhaps explains her shameless air in church for the situation is now quite familiar to her. Fortunately her childbearing years will soon be at an end.

It was a gratifyingly bright day today and it was with considerable pleasure that I strolled down to the Rectory for luncheon after the service. After a turn around the garden we were served with galantine followed by a suet pudding and I ventured to send my compliments to Mrs Molland in the kitchen.

The afternoon proved most elucidating. Reverend Harding and I visited seven households in all, being those most in need of prayer and solace as a result of the fever. As on previous occasions, it was an education for me to watch his ways with the common people. He understands their customs and their concerns better than I and displays such a genuine warmth towards them, placing his hand on the shoulder or arm and looking into the eyes, that they cannot help but respond. I would like very much to emulate his ways and pray for the courage to do so.

There were many touching incidents during the afternoon. Reverend Harding spoke most kindly to Mr and Mrs Dennis about Sarah and the engaging little ways she used to exhibit, until Mr Dennis, who has until now remained in a benumbed silence, joined in with the enumeration of her charms with great emotion and for the first time participated most fervently when we prayed together for acceptance. It was again a distressing scene with Mrs Powe. It was only she to whom we spoke as the other three members of the family were upstairs with the fever. It seems that her son is past the worst although he remains in a weakened state. Mary, who is eleven years old, is very unwell and her mother fears for her and also for her husband who, unusually for a grown man, now shows all the symptoms of scarlet fever.

Monday 30th January 1871.
I have, today, felt a greater sense of purpose than I have

experienced for some time. I awoke early and, noticing from my window that the sky was clear and bright, descended for some fresh air before breakfast. It is not often that I leave my rooms without a precise purpose, especially so early in the day, and Mrs Heywood, who was already busy preparing food as I passed through the kitchen, expressed considerable surprise in her usual effusive manner. It was strange and not unpleasant to witness scenes of great assiduity as I took a turn through the yard and down to the orchard, and I found it singular that such industry and good-humoured banter is taking place each morning while I am confined with my books in my obscure, silent room. Here all was bustle and purpose, with cows to milk, butter to churn, buckets to carry and comments on the progress of the work to be shouted merrily from place to place. Even the serious, hardworking child, Ann Williams, managed a cheery "good morning" as she carried a bath of water with her brother - though I afterwards heard her scold him wholeheartedly for slopping the water on her feet. I resolved to descend from my rooms more often and become more familiar with the ways of the common people. I am sure, too, that if I did so my presence would not cause the sense of unease that I perceived this morning.

After a breakfast of bacon, kidneys and freshly baked bread, I rested for a short while then descended again to find Bruno saddled and waiting for me. The ride to Bideford was pleasant enough, with the exception of some young urchins in the old town who threw stones perilously close to my horse's legs and ran away laughing before I could think of a suitable rebuke. I must keep it in mind to carry my whip on the next occasion.

I had determined without further ado to order provisions with the money that Mr Harding had given me for that purpose, although I am disposed to think that the worst of the fever has now passed. It will, in any case, be useful to me to keep a small store of such things, so that I may give aid to those in need without delay. It is true that I have, in the past, experienced some misgivings as to the wisdom of acting in this capacity, but having been reminded of the high regard in which Mr Harding is held amongst the cottagers, who see him as a true man of God as well as a provider of alms, I feel I must reconcile myself to such a role.

The town was pleasantly busy with three or four conveyances drawn up on the Quay in addition to some half a dozen horses tethered at intervals. There were two ships moored, the unloading of one being the cause of considerable activity and uproar. From the far bank of the river a reverberating beat came from Mr Johnson's boatyard and the whole, together with the rhythmic clatter and clouds of steam that rose from an approaching train, presented a scene of significant interest. I intend to visit the town more often, for I am sure that my isolation in Littleham does not encourage a purposeful state of mind, especially as intelligent men with whom I may converse are a rarity in these parts.

I found it most enjoyable to pass from shop to shop, consulting with the shopkeepers and making my purchases, especially as I so rarely have cause to perform such tasks. In Pedler and Heywood's drapers I was shown such an array of blankets that the effort of making a choice almost made my head spin, but the matron who was attending to me helped me select a dozen which she assured me would be serviceable, without using all the money I had available. From there I passed to Wickham's wine merchants for port wine and a little brandy then down to Mrs Emma Cooler's greengrocers where I purchased a box of oranges. In Mill Street I met with Mr James Colwill who is curate at Buckland Brewer and we conversed at length on the course of the fever which is affecting his parish also, although it has now passed from Bideford. He invited me to dine on Thursday next, an offer which I accepted gratefully.

As it was now approaching time for luncheon, I informed the boy who was minding my horse that I should be some time longer. I then made my way to Mr Lee's Refreshment House in the Market Square, an establishment that, though humble, I have heard recommended on a number of occasions. I found it quiet, there not being a market today, of which I was glad. I was served with a very good mutton stew with carrots and potatoes, by a dark-haired young woman who passed the time of day with me most pleasantly. After luncheon I arranged with the carrier for my purchases to be collected and delivered to Littleham Court, a service which was completed later this afternoon.

On my ride home I overtook blind John Westcott returning to his cottage from some simple errand that he performs from time to time for Mrs Heywood. His back is so bowed from a lifetime of load-carrying that when approached from behind, he appears as some half-creature with legs and lower body only, a most curious sight. I shouted a greeting as loud as I felt able but his hearing seems quite gone now and he remained unaware of my passing.

This evening I read through some sermons and wrote my Journal up to the present time. Tomorrow I shall visit those most in need; Mrs Powe, the Piper family and Mrs Vilot at East Furlong Cottage and I shall try to communicate the love of God with the same sense of warmth and understanding as does the Reverend Harding. May God stand by me and help me to find the courage I have lacked.

# CHAPTER FIVE

Today, Mount Pleasant has a peaceful, pleasant aspect. The long, low terrace of small-windowed cottages is set on a south-facing slope and on a sunny day the uniform whiteness of their facades is dazzling, offset in summer by tubs and baskets of flowers. It was on this terrace that much of my interest centred, both because some of the families that most intrigued me had lived there, and because I had lived there myself for many years.

Mount Pleasant is situated half way between the pub, the Crealock Arms, at one end of the village and the village hall at the other. Although Littleham has no real centre, the terrace could certainly be described as central. When I first moved to Littleham, Mount Pleasant was referred to, by those whose roots in the village stretched back to 1900 and beyond, as "the village" and seemed to be considered the focal point of the surrounding area. It may be that the same was true in the nineteenth century if only because of the density of population; in 1871 53 people lived in the terrace, as compared with 18 in the same houses today.

It is commonly thought that the cottages are very old. Dating them accurately is difficult without expert guidance, as their designs and building materials are typical of those in use throughout the eighteenth and nineteenth century. I obtained the deeds and other papers including old wills relating to my house, and spent many hours poring over the huge documents, struggling with pointed finger to keep my place in paragraphs a metre wide while trying to absorb the convoluted and confusing language. I was unable to reach any definite conclusions until I borrowed deeds from a neighbour, which yielded additional information that confirmed, as far as I could tell, that Mount Pleasant was built in 1828. This tallied with the Births and Baptisms Registers where the first mention of Mount Pleasant was in 1829, and also with a map of 1827 on which the cottages were not shown. The row actually consists of two short terraces and in the 1841 census the names "Mount Pleasant" and "Smiths Row" were used but the latter name was later dropped.

Intimations of the past can be found throughout Mount Pleasant. Much of the modernisation which was carried out, as was the fashion, in the 1950's and 60's has now been reversed; small tiled fireplaces removed to reveal the original large inglenooks and bread ovens behind; plasterboard ceilings pulled down to find the beams which would once have been covered with lath and plaster. The interiors of all the cottages would once have been very similar; the central front door opening straight into the main room with the huge fireplace forming one wall, a smaller room no more than six or eight feet wide opening off that, a scullery at the back and stairs leading to two bedrooms. Two cottages were smaller and contained only one room downstairs and one up. These smaller cottages have now been incorporated with their neighbours, and in many houses the two lower rooms have been made into one and larger kitchens and new bathrooms added at the back. In all the cottages there are strange idiosyncrasies which cause the owners to wonder about the original layout. In one a tiny fireplace was found while the area under the stairs was being replastered; in another a blocked-in window stares blindly into what is now a garage; in several, there are strange cupboards in the walls alongside the fireplaces which resemble windows, but are set in party walls.

Originally the cottages would have been thatched. I was unable to find any early photographs except for one from about the 1940's showing only the westernmost of the cottages, and it was indeed thatched at that time. Before concrete became available, the floors were of earth; a less inconvenient solution than may be thought as well-trodden earth floors, providing they can be kept dry, develop a hard sheen not unlike polished wood. Without electricity the inhabitants would have been reliant on an ever-glowing fire in the inglenook for cooking, and on candles and, later, oil lamps for light. Water was carried from a well a hundred yards away in buckets or two-handled tubs known as trays, a daily chore which had to be performed whatever the weather and however old or frail the bearer. One cottage had - and still has - a pump of its own in the back garden from which immediate neighbours were entitled to fetch water.

All the cottages have good-sized rear gardens which, being situated on a south-facing slope, are sunny and sheltered. The soil is good, having been cultivated for two hundred years, and although most of the gardens now bear a profusion of flowers and shrubs, they are also capable of producing most of the vegetables needed to sustain a family. Some of the gardens still retain at their far end an old, stone outbuilding with low, sloping tiled roof; these now contain logs and garden implements but would have originally housed the earth closet, a function which continued until mains water first reached the village in 1949.

The census was, of course, the most valuable source of information as I struggled to find out more about the inhabitants of 1871. It was difficult to work out which family inhabited which cottage as the cottages were not then numbered - it would not have been necessary at a time when everyone knew everyone else and letters were rarely received. I supposed at first that the census enumerator would work his way through the village in a logical manner. However when I compared the results with the censuses of 1861 and 1881, they made no sense at all. I knew that people could move from one house to another within the terrace - I had done so myself as had others within living memory, but I could not believe that anyone moved from the westernmost house to the easternmost and back again while others swapped houses with their neighbours then changed back again. The answer seemed to be that the enumerator did not always proceed in the expected manner. I drew diagrams of the cottages with the names of their inhabitants for 1861, '71 and '81 and tried to fit them together like a jigsaw puzzle, comparing them with the names in the old deeds of my house. Still there was no obvious solution. It occurred to me in a moment of despair that the enumerator knocked at the doors of cottages up and down the terrace in a completely random order as the whim took him.

Some families particularly interested me. William Westcott, a carpenter, and his wife Maria were born in Littleham and lived there all their lives, producing seven children. Their descendants still live in the village today. They first appeared in the census for Mount Pleasant in 1851 and remained in the terrace for the next forty years. I found their shared gravestone in the churchyard; Maria died in 1890 aged sixty and William in 1896 aged seventy-six. At the time of the 1871 census, three of their seven children were living at home; Harry, aged four, Alice, aged 11 and Thomas, aged 14. The family lived in the middle of the larger terrace. I was able to identify the cottage by cross-referencing the census returns with the deeds of my own house, which was, until 1930, two cottages of four and two rooms respectively. William Westcott lived in the larger of these. At the front it can be seen that part of the garden wall has been filled in where the old entrance led through the narrow front garden. Beyond it the ghostly shadow of the original front door can be discerned, corresponding with a cupboard inside which has utilised the space in the thick wall. The boarded ceiling of the living room has a join running across its width where a wall once stood, dividing the room into two. Newer boards of a different design fill the space where the stairs would have been. Perhaps it was William Westcott who dug the well and installed the pump outside the kitchen door. With seven children to feed, every inch of the garden would have been cultivated for vegetables and perhaps a pig was kept at the end of the garden alongside the privy, in the outhouse where my children had kept a rabbit. When I dig the garden on warm spring evenings I sometimes pause and lean on the spade to imagine William Westcott working alongside me, separated only by time.

It is likely that, as a carpenter, William Westcott was relatively well off when compared with his neighbours, many of whom were labourers. The average weekly wage for a carpenter at this time was in the region of twenty-five shillings a week, though wages in Devon were generally lower than in many other parts of the country. I was unable to discover whether he had a workshop behind the cottage or whether he worked with either of the other two carpenters who lived in the village in 1871 - in earlier years there had been as many as six at any one time. There would have been plenty of work with so many small farms in the area, all of which would have needed new or repaired troughs, gates, milking stools, buckets and ladders; households required new windows and doors; housemaids leaving home to go into service needed wooden travelling boxes; and it was generally the village carpenter who made coffins. William Westcott would have had a busy year in 1871.

The Westcotts rented the cottage from John Hookaway. John Hookaway, although a farm labourer, owned the lease on four cottages one of which he inhabited himself with his wife Grace. He had acquired the lease of the land in 1827 and the cottages were built shortly after this date, perhaps by John himself with the help of those villagers who wished to lease them. In 1871, Grace, by then a widow aged eighty, was described as a shopkeeper and shared her Mount Pleasant cottage with a seventy-year-old spinster, Sarah Brooks. She lived next door to the Westcott family in, as far as I could tell, the two-roomed cottage that was now part of my own house. If the downstairs room was also being used as a shop, it must have been a very cramped household. This was not the only shop in the village, the other being run by a widow, Mary Walters, in one of three dwellings which have since disappeared, known as East Furlong Cottages. It is likely that both shops sold all the basic goods that local families were likely to require, from tea, tobacco and sweets to coal, candles and soap. Most families would also have made a weekly trip on foot to Bideford for the greater range of goods, lower prices and opportunities for social contact such a visit afforded, but the village shops would have had the advantage of offering credit. It was common for these debts to remain outstanding for many years, as shown by one example of many quoted in *"The Shearers and the Shorn: a Study of Life in a Devon Community"* by E.W. Martin.

"An agricultural labourer who had bought bread, tea, cheese, corned beef, tobacco, flour and other goods from his local shop owed £2 18s. at the end of 1895. By the end of 1896 the debt had increased to £6 6s. 6d. Throughout 1897 he was struggling with irregular payments and managed to reduce the amount to £4 10s., having been able to pay 10s by means of a ticket from a local charity. In 1907 he paid another 10s from the same charity. But throughout 1908 he owed 18s., and did not settle the debt entirely until May 1911."

It would not have been easy for shopkeepers to make a living in such circumstances. Grace Hookaway would at least have had the rental income from three other cottages and would, therefore, have been relatively comfortable. The same could certainly not be said of all the families in Mount Pleasant. Probably the poorest sector of the working population in nineteenth century rural England was the farm labourers. William Piper and his family lived in a Mount Pleasant cottage with his wife, six daughters aged between 12 months and 23 years, and one son of four years. The eldest daughter worked as a glover but the other children were all described as scholars. There had been two other daughters in the previous census, who would perhaps have been working away from home in service by 1871, when they would have been aged 19 and 21. It is to be hoped that some, if not all, their wages were sent home to their parents as it hard to see otherwise how the family could have survived.

Farm labourers' wages varied in different parts of the country, being higher in the north of England where they had to compete with the wages paid in industry and where there was comparatively less labour available. Pay in the southwest was much lower, a weekly wage of 11s. a week being normal in Devon in 1871. A year later, Joseph Arch would found the National Agricultural Labourers' Union, which would in time bring about an improvement in pay and reduction in working hours but William Piper knew nothing of that in 1871. His weekly wage was equal in purchasing power to about £30 today. He would have been able to earn a little more in the summer when hay making and harvesting. Life was altogether easier in the summer with the weather more congenial to outdoor work, plenty of vegetables to eat from the cottage garden and less fuel needed for the fire which was lit only for cooking. In the winter, life could be grim indeed. Of his 11s. weekly wage, approximately 1s. 6d or 2s. would have to be paid in rent, a comparatively low sum which did not encourage the landlord to spend anything on upkeep and consequently many houses were in a poor state of repair. Unlike today, when the major expenditure in most family incomes is the rent or mortgage repayments, most of his wages would have been spent on food for the family. His weekly expenditure would have looked something like this:

|  | s | d |
|---|---|---|
| Rent | 1 | 06 |
| Flour | 6 | 10 |
| Yeast |  | 03 |
| Cheese | 1 | 00 |
| Bacon | 1 | 06 |
| Tea |  | 06 |
| Coal |  | 10 |
| Soap, soda |  | 01 |
|  | 12s | 06d |

It is immediately apparent that the family did not have a varied diet. The main expenditure was flour, as each adult would have eaten five or six kilos of bread a week, several slices for breakfast, dinner and tea and very little with it; a little skimmed milk cheese perhaps, a cube of bacon for the man of the house, perhaps an onion from the garden. The children rarely had milk and it was common for them to go to bed hungry. Some of the flour would be used to make puddings and potato pasties, and sometimes potatoes and other vegetables from the garden were made into a stew. If the family kept a pig, as did all that could possibly manage it, bacon would appear on the plate more often and even the children would have some. When there was a pig in the outhouse at the end of the garden it was a focus of interest for the whole family; it was fed on vegetable water and peelings from the kitchen and armfuls of grass and weeds collected by the children on their way home from school. When it was killed everyone was kept busy for several days making hogs puddings and chitterlings and salting the sides of bacon; some would be sold to raise enough money to buy the next piglet for fattening. If the family found themselves in debt through illness or a new baby in the family, the whole pig might have to be sold to pay the rent.

Richard Jefferies, the Wiltshire farmer and eminent writer on the Victorian countryside, stated in "*The Toilers of the Field*" in 1892 that the simple ingredients available to the agricultural labourer were not improved by the preparation and cooking they received.

"There is nothing," he wrote "connected with the condition of the agricultural poor that is better worth the attention of improvers than the style of cooking pursued in these cottages. A more wretched cookery probably does not exist on the face of this earth. The soddened cabbage is typical of the whole thing."

Even on this meagre and unappetising diet, William Piper has overspent by 1s 6d a week. He probably did occasional odd jobs to earn a few more pennies when it was light enough in the evenings, or at weekends if he could afford the time away from tilling his garden. His wife might take in washing for one of her wealthier neighbours in order to earn 6d one day a week. Fortunately his oldest daughter was a glovemaker; if she was good at her work and kept at it for ten or twelve hours a day, she would have earned about 5s a week. Along with any odd jobs the children might do on nearby farms - though he was disadvantaged by having six daughters - this would have brought in an additional six or seven shillings a week. With this he would - if he saved - be able to buy a pair of boots at 14s a pair for the next oldest daughter, Emma, so that she could go to school. As these boots were outgrown they could be repaired and renailed as they were handed on down the family. In the meantime the children would often stay at home barefooted for lack of suitable footwear, for although it was acceptable to go barefoot around the village, boots were necessary for school. Clothes were less of a problem, there was no money to buy any for the children so the parents' old clothes and clothes donated by local clergy and gentry were cut down and remade.

Two children walk along the lane past my window, chattering and laughing. I go outside and watch as the girls pass down the road, their brisk walk interspersed by an occasional hop and skip. Their shiny brown hair swings from brightly-coloured plastic clips and their perfectly matched blue and pink skirts sway in confident rhythm. One looks at her watch and comes to a sudden halt, clutching her friend's arm in horror.

"It's time for Neighbours!"

They break into a run and the rhythmic clatter of their heels fades as they disappear round the corner.

Only four children live in Mount Pleasant now, as compared with 26 in 1871. Most lived in what we would now consider to be grossly overcrowded conditions; William and Elizabeth Piper had two bedrooms for themselves and seven children. James Lee, a farm labourer, and his wife Harriet lived in the cottage now known as number nine. They shared their two bedrooms with their three sons, one daughter and Harriet's mother who, as a monthly nurse, would have earned a few shillings to contribute to the household by looking after newly delivered mothers. It was common for one bedroom to be divided by hanging a sheet across its length; perhaps grandmother and granddaughter shared a bed in one half of the small room, leaving the other half for the three boys. A similar arrangement would have been made in number seven where Albert Dennis, a labourer at Apps Brewery in the village, shared his two-bedroomed cottage with his wife Amelia, her mother, and their four children. His mother in law, Judith Grigg, aged 76 is described in the census as an annuitant. There were of course no state pensions so elderly people had to carry on working for as long as they were able and then rely on their families or appeal to the Overseers of the Poor. At worst they ended their days in the workhouse. Judith must have been in receipt of an annual payment that may have been only a few shillings, possibly as a result of a little money invested for the purpose by her husband.

Whether the overcrowded sleeping conditions in labourers' cottages gave rise to "gross immorality", as was often claimed by those in more fortunate circumstances, is only possible to gauge by reading reliable contemporary accounts. What was apparent from the census and the Register of Baptisms, however, was the surprisingly high number of illegitimate births, usually described as "baseborn" in the Register. There were eight children in Littleham in 1871 who had been born out of wedlock, representing 5.2% of all children of fourteen and under. In 1861 the percentage had been 8%, figures that seems strangely at odds with the prevailing view of Victorian England as a highly respectable society. Respectability was of course far easier for the rich to attain than for the poor - most of the illegitimate children were born to the daughters of labourers rather than farmers or landowners. Richard Jefferies wrote in "*The Toilers of the Field*"

"The overcrowding in cottages leads to what may be called an indifference to decency... stern necessity leads to a coarseness and indelicacy which hardens the minds and deadens the natural modesty of even the best girls... The girl who has had an illegitimate child is thought very little the worse of by her friends and her own class, especially if her seducer is a man who can afford to pay for it - that is the grand point. If she is fool enough to yield to a man who is badly off, she may be jeered at as a fool, but rarely reprimanded as a sinner, not even by her own mother. Such things are not looked upon by the rural poor as sins, but as accidents of their condition."

In Littleham, the sisters of William Piper could be seen as typical, if unusually prolific examples of those who had illegitimate children. Their parents, William Piper, a farm labourer, and his wife Ann had lived at Furlong Farm when their son William was born. They must then have fallen on hard times for their three daughters, Mary, Ann and Maria were born between 1829 and 1834 in the Littleham Poor House, a cottage which once stood alongside the church. By 1851 the family were living in Mount Pleasant, all three daughters, then aged 21, 19 and 17 years, were described as "gloveresses" and Mary had had her first "baseborn" son, Samuel. From then on, the girls' names appeared frequently in the Register of Baptisms; Mary gave birth to another son, John, in 1855 and had further illegitimate children baptised in 1858, '60, '65 and '71, Ann in '54, '57 and '65, and Maria had one in '55. Two of Ann's three children died in infancy. When I consulted the 1881 census, I found Mary, by then described as a washerwoman, living in Meddon Street in Bideford with a further three illegitimate children; she was then aged 48 so perhaps nine children was her final tally.

According to the census returns, at no time were any of women cohabiting with men and the identity of the fathers of the children remains a mystery. It would not have been easy for the women to support the children themselves and it may be that the overseers of the poor granted them aid from time to time. All three worked as glovers, the usual occupation in the Littleham area for widows and unmarried women with children, as it was work undertaken at home which could therefore be combined with looking after children. It was also an alternative to domestic service for young unmarried women living with their parents and almost all women listed in the Littleham Register of Marriages in the middle of the nineteenth century were described as glovers at the time of their marriage. There was a limited choice of employment for women; some seasonal employment in agriculture, dressmaking, or taking in washing and ironing for wealthier neighbours. The latter was backbreaking work as all the water had to be carried from the village pump and heated on a fire or furnace, the clothes scrubbed and rinsed by hand, gradually dried around the fire when the weather was wet and finally ironed with irons heated by the fire.

There were glove factories in Bideford and Torrington. It was a major industry that had grown up in the seventeenth century alongside the flourishing wool trade, which it eventually overtook. In 1871 there were just over two thousand women employed as glovers in Devon, and one Torrington factory alone employed eight hundred workers, many of them working in their own homes. The materials were prepared and the gloves cut out in the factory, these were then delivered to homes throughout the area by a pack woman who also collected the finished gloves. There were nine "gloveresses" in Littleham in 1871 and 24 ten years previously; in the earlier census they were described as making gloves either of "thread and silk" or "any kind". The true numbers were probably somewhat higher than this as married women who combined part time gloving with looking after the home would have been unlikely to declare their occupation in the census return. According to Pamela Horn in *"The Victorian Country Child"* it was also common for daughters to help their mothers with the gloving; these children would nevertheless be described as "scholars" in the census. She quotes a schoolmistress in Somerset who asked her class how many of them worked at gloving in the evening:

"every girl, even a little thing of eight, held up her hand. She worked every evening from 5 p.m. to 9 p.m."

It was close work that was liable to cause eyestrain, as the stitches, both functional and decorative, were required to be very tiny. The long hours of immobility often led to chilblains in winter months. Neither was it well paid; one source suggests a worker in 1864 might expect to get 3s 6d for a dozen pairs of gloves, but she could only make two pairs a day, working for ten or twelve hours a day. Another contemporary source in 1885 claimed a woman working all day could make one and a half or two dozen pairs a week and earn 5s to 7s per week. A male glover working in the factory could expect a weekly wage of about 15s a week. In all areas of employment, male wages were far higher than female and it was sometimes stated that a man's weekly wage equalled that of a boy's, a girl's and a woman's, added together.

Gloving did afford single women a measure of independence. Whereas women who worked in domestic service were subject to strict rules of conduct, being obliged to dress neatly and speak and act with decorum while in their employers' houses, gloveresses were subject to no rules but their own. If several in the household were employed, they would sometimes have a portion of their income to spend as they wished. This freedom led, from time to time, to charges of immorality which were perhaps partially rooted in fact, but also in the resentment felt by middle class employers who found it more difficult to find servants in areas where gloving was carried out, and who desired to keep the working classes, especially women, firmly in their place. One criticism of Torrington gloveresses in 1859 was strongly refuted and led to a public outcry; it is however interesting for the light it throws on the gloving industry. The letter by J.C. Moore-Stevens of Torrington was published in the *North Devon Journal* of 17th March 1859, having previously been published in the Gloucester Journal.

"Winscott, Great Torrington, N. Devon, Feb. 20, 1859.
Sir, I can indorse every portion of your excellent letter. I consider the Glove Trade the great curse of the town and neighbourhood of Great Torrington.
But I will answer your question seriatim,

157

I consider the gloving trade tends to demoralise the young girls engaged in it; totally unfits them for any honest occupation; they live at home with their parents, spend their earnings in dress, gin, etc. They work at home all day, and at night turn out upon the town. The girls from the country are brought into the town, and there become demoralised. If married, they are bad wives and improvident mothers, and we cannot induce them, as formerly to employ themselves in the healthy employment of agriculture. We find it impossible to obtain domestic servants here, whereas formerly plenty of excellent servants could always be procured. I believe the wages average from 2s to 7s per week, I believe bastardy on the increase, I sat as a magistate to adjudicate on three cases in one morning, and I never heard such fearful perjury before. If you have any regard for the well being of Gloucester, above all keep off the gloving trade.

I am, sir, your faithful servant,

    J.C.M. STEVENS."

It is obvious that the letter was written in a hurry, and it was, in fact, never intended for publication, as is made clear in an enquiry into the circumstances surrounding the letter, published by the Report and Transactions of the Devonshire Association in December 1992. Although the claims made in the letter reflect on the writer as much as the gloveresses, this was the not the only such criticism. A novel written by the popular writer Mrs Henry Wood in 1862, "*Mrs Halliburton's Troubles*", has as its background the gloving industry in "Helstonleigh", a town based on Worcester. Although it features many hard-working men and women, including the heroine of the novel, a widow with three children forced to turn to gloving for survival, the young gloveresses working at home come in for marked criticism throughout the novel. One example, in which Mrs Buffle, a shopkeeper, warns Mrs Halliburton of the gloveresses' ways, will suffice:

"They be the improvidentest things in the world, mum, these gloveress girls. Sundays they be dressed up as grand as queens, flowers inside their bonnets, and ribbuns out, a-setting the churches and chapels alight with their finery; and then off for walks with their sweethearts, all the afternoon and evening. Mondays is mostly spent in waste, gathering of themselves at each other's houses, talking and laughing, or, may be, off to the fields again - anything for idleness. Tuesdays is often the same, and then the rest of the week they has to scout over their work, to get it in on the Saturday. Ah! you don't know 'em, mum."

Whether this was the way of the gloveresses in Littleham, we shall probably never know. It may be that the ability to pass days in idleness and to spend money on ribbons or gin was dependant on the father of the household earning a good wage, so that the day to day survival of the family was not dependant on the income from gloving. This was not likely to be the case when the father was a farm labourer. As for the charges of immorality, also made in areas where straw-plaiting was prevalent, it is as likely that girls who had a "baseborn" child turned to gloving to support themselves, domestic service no longer being possible, than the gloving in some way brought about their "immorality". Certainly this would not have been the intention of the employers. The owner of one glove factory in Torrington, William Vaughan, was an ardent Bible Christian and designed his factory in Whites Lane to resemble a chapel.

The Powe family were neighbours of William Piper in Mount Pleasant in 1871. The Powes were not originally a Littleham family, William having been brought up in Peter's Marland some ten miles away and Martha probably in Bradworthy. They must have felt like outsiders or "vurriners" when they first moved into Mount Pleasant, for most of the inhabitants of the terrace, including the Westcotts and Hookaways, had strong Littleham connections. Of the 27 adults living in Mount Pleasant, 13 had been born in Littleham and another six in villages no more than three miles away, and 22 of the 26 children had been born in the village. William Powe would no doubt have moved to Littleham in order to take up the offer of work at the Rectory, as this was the most usual reason for a move. Whereas today almost all employees in Littleham work outside the village, the opposite was true in 1871. Few would have chosen to live in the village if they worked in Bideford, involving as it did a three mile walk along frequently muddy tracks and lanes, wearing heavy boots and clothes which failed to keep out the rain and which quickly became heavy and cumbersome. This walk would have to be undertaken in the dark for part of the year, as a twelve-hour working day was quite usual.

In 1871 Mount Pleasant only contained two people, a miner and a pottery labourer, who one could assume to be working outside the village, as it was not possible to practise these trades in Littleham. There was, however, a pottery at Hallsannery, two miles away. *Morris's Directory* for 1870 carried an advertisement for

"Bryant Ching, Manufacturer of Fire Clay Ovens, Garden Pots, Agricultural Draining pipes, Chimney Pots, Tiles and Earthenware. Hall's Annery Potteries, Bideford."

It is likely that all other employees in Mount Pleasant were working in the village. There were three farm labourers, a general labourer and a brewery labourer, an 18 year old blacksmith, a monthly nurse, a washerwoman - a widow living alone -, a yeoman, a shoemaker, a shopkeeper, a carpenter, three gloveresses and a mason. It is significant that all were engaged in manual work and a quick glance at the census returns for the rest of the village shows that Mount Pleasant was typical; there were no professional people in Littleham in 1871. It was not generally considered desirable among the middle classes to live out of town unless one could afford a large country house with extensive grounds, perhaps so that the unsightly poor might be kept at a safe distance. Today the cottages are not generally available to rent and property prices have recently increased to a level which is way beyond that which could be afforded by those in manual trades. When I look at the immaculate flower-bedecked houses, each with a shiny car parked alongside its old stone garden wall, I wonder what William Piper would have said.

# The Diary of James H. Andrew, Curate of Littleham

<u>Thursday 9th February 1871.</u>

I hardly know where to start in writing this Journal, or indeed whether it is advisable to write it at all, when my time might be better used in practical matters, or in prayer. However the writing of it is, I think, beneficial in calming my nerves and in aiding me to order my thoughts; it may also be that my account will be of interest to me in the future when I am able to reflect on the events in this village. I will not dwell, however, on the last ten days. My precipitous departure from Littleham upon receiving my sister's letter and my distress at finding my mother so indisposed have taken their toll upon both my health and my nerves and it seems that there is to be no abatement. When I finally reached the shelter of Littleham Court yesterday, jaded from the rigours of travel, to learn that the fever has renewed its strength, I confess I felt close to despair and felt so much exhausted by the exertions of the day that I went early to bed.

Mrs Heywood informed me of the latest developments when she brought me my breakfast this morning. Her insistence on communicating the daily events piecemeal along with her opinions on every matter, instead of leaving me to eat my breakfast in peace led me to experience a considerable degree of indigestion by the time I had finished eating. It was some time before I felt equal to the task of venturing into the village.

I chose to walk in order to calm myself. It has been a mild, fine day with a light south-westerly breeze. I saw the first daffodils pushing aside the litter of dead leaves deep in the hedge bank and I wished that I could spend the entire day walking. In my anxious state it seemed to me that the fields around the village were emptier than usual of workers as if all stayed at home to sit at deathbeds, for I saw no one on my walk; no chanting came from the Methodist schoolroom; no children played in the mud at the cross-roads. As I passed East Furlong Cottages a young woman holding a baby came out and greeted me. She had a pleasant, gracious manner for a cottage girl. She enquired whether I was intending to visit Mrs Martha Powe and, when I replied that I was, asked whether I might take a gift with me on her behalf. She returned with an apple pie on a plate, explaining that Mrs Powe was a friend of hers, but that she dared not visit for fear of her own children contracting the fever. She was a comely girl with most eloquent eyes that brimmed with tears as she spoke. Her name, she said, was Mrs Lucy Glover, her husband being the brother of George Glover, the young blacksmith. I felt somewhat foolish as I walked on carrying the plate precariously in one hand and my stick in the other and was glad that the village street was devoid of passers-by.

Young William Powe answered my knock and I was glad to see that he, at least, is recovered, though looking pale and tired. He ran upstairs and I passed into the main room of the cottage where smoke from a badly tended fire hung in the air. Mrs Martha Powe descended the narrow staircase and I was shocked at her appearance for she seemed to have advanced greatly in age and her eyes were dull from fatigue and grief. She asked me to see her daughter Mary and when I questioned the wisdom of this, she replied most feelingly,

"Sir, please, there's nought to do but pray for her soul."

The scene in the room above was pitiful. It was apparent that Mary was in a dying state, as I had feared, for Mrs Heywood had explained that the scarlet fever had been followed by a further infection. As I prayed at her bedside she followed some of the familiar prayers with her lips although her eyes remained closed and her breath came fast and shallow. I spoke of her sisters, Elizabeth and Ellen, safe with the Lord; at this she seemed to stir a little and her mother took her hand, telling her she would soon see her sisters again,

"and one day us'll *all* be together again."

The mother seemed unable to cry, for which I was thankful, but drew slow shuddering breaths as she gazed at the sad spectacle before her.

On the direction of a female relative who was also in the room, I passed into the second chamber, where lay the father. He was conscious but in a very weakened state, his face pale, sunken and hollow and his eyes lacklustre. I could not find the words to greet him but knelt at his bedside and prayed. I fear the poor fellow is sick with sorrow as much as fever, for it is rare for this illness to affect a grown man in such a way. I found myself at a loss knowing whether to urge him to rouse himself for the sake of his wife and son or to accept God's will. I left after a short while. My prayers, I hope, helped Mary as she hastens to that abode from which no traveller returns, but I fear I have provided little comfort for her parents.

I called also at the house of James Lee at the far end of Mount Pleasant where three young children have the fever. He was at work in the fields for money must be earned. It seems the children may be past the worst but I could gain little information, for Mrs Harriet Lee was timid and fearful in the extreme and I was not invited to enter the house. She was exceedingly thin with a grey unhealthy look about her face. From here I went on to the blessed haven of the church and spent some time in prayer and quiet contemplation.

After luncheon I went out again, on horseback this time, calling at John Quick's cottage on Moorehead Hill and Mary Piper at Polland's Cottage with gifts of blankets, for I had been told that both households have the fever. However Mary Piper's fatherless son was playing on the doorstep when I arrived. She and her aged parents are ever quick to ask for alms. I must plan a suitable reply in the event of her pleading further hardship.

I rode back, then, to Edge Mill. I had received a message

asking me to call, which perplexed me somewhat for the family is Methodist as is usual amongst the farmers. The poorer Methodists, it is true, will sometimes ask to see the clergy when ill or distressed for we so often bring pecuniary advantages, but I knew that the Molland family would not be moved by such considerations. I have never visited the place before and it was with some trepidation that I rode down the track from the Bradworthy Road. I found the mill and farmhouse lying in a delightful position beside the River Yeo, obscured from sight by the row of cottages that lines the road above. It was a scene that combined industry and tranquillity in most pleasing proportions; the placid river bordered by overarching trees winding through the fertile valley; the white ducks crouching at the edge of the greensward that sloped from the tidy house; the deep vibrating hum and rush of sparkling water from the mill; the energetic young farm hand chopping wood at the log room door; all served to remind me of God's blessing in allowing me to work in an area so rich in natural advantages.

As I dismounted, James Molland came out of the mill and strode towards me, shaking my hand and declaring,

"Bless your heart, sir, we are glad to see you."

He explained that there are six children in the family, the eldest being eight years of age and the youngest a babe of just a few weeks. He and his wife were fearful, for the youngest was not yet baptised and two children now had the fever. He did not say, but I knew that the Methodist minister, living at a distance, would not be able to come as quickly as I. I promised to call again to carry out the ceremony and he thanked me kindly.

I returned home and have felt most weary despite a good dinner of ham and potatoes. With so many sick, there is much work for me to do yet few are willing to cast themselves upon Christ as their salvation and their hope despite my prayers. The Reverend Harding communicates the love of God with his eyes and his touch. I try to emulate his ways but I have only words and even they fail me on occasion; then, I can utter prayers but can find no warm-hearted words of human comfort.

Friday 10th February 1871.
A dark day. Mary Powe died this afternoon after a long struggle. I stayed in the house throughout her last hours. She was not granted serenity as she passed to her eternal rest, nor her parents a peaceful acceptance of her going. I confess the scene was quite terrible, and can only pray that her parents' suffering will bring them closer to God. I prayed aloud throughout but there were times when my words sounded meaningless, even to my ears. I read 1 Cor. XV 55-57.

"O death, where is thy sting? O grave, where is thy victory? The sting of death is sin; and the strength of sin is the law. But thanks be to God, which giveth us the victory through our Lord Jesus Christ."

Would that I could have believed the words at that moment for there, before me, was both the sting and the victory of death.

Dr Ackland was present. He endeavoured, in a last desperate measure, to apply leeches to Mary's throat, but in vain. It was a scene that will always haunt me; the girl's fearful struggle, the father's sobs, the mother's paroxysms of grief. I could do nothing for them.

When her ordeal had at last ended and I had said the final prayers, I left quietly and without farewells. Downstairs I found William crouched terror-stricken and silent by the cold hearth. Not one of us had considered him during the passing of his last remaining sister.

I go early to bed tonight and have not the stomach for food.

Saturday 11th February 1871.
Arthur Molland, aged six years, of Edge Mill died last night. The news had not reached me but the mill was silent when I arrived, the river melancholy in the rain. I was given the news by the housemaid, no more than a frightened child

165

herself, who opened the door to me. I baptised Rosa Jane in the kitchen. She cried throughout, a tiny child swathed in shawls, far younger than the usual age for baptism. Two more of their children have the fever. I spoke, without conviction I fear, of the opportunity to experience loss as a spiritual challenge, which could lead to purification of the soul. The mother gave me a wild look, as if I might have lost my mind.

I spent the remainder of the day visiting the sick. It appears that for every child who recovers, another falls sick. There are also two more adults with the fever. The village is silent and fearful. I met with Dr Ackland three times during the course of my visits. He seems almost cheerful as he goes about his business.

Tonight my throat aches and I have a fearful headache.

Sunday 12th February 1871.

I performed the service this morning and conducted the funerals of Mary Powe and William Molland this afternoon. One funeral immediately followed the other and some of the small number of mourners attended both. I was so oppressed at the chest and hoarse in the voice owing to my cold, it was a struggle to reach the end.

I am wearied by so much death and suffering.

Monday 13th February 1871.

I received a letter from my sister this morning informing me that my mother continues her recovery, news for which I thanked God most heartily. My own health is still poor and I have reached the decision to leave off meat and all stimulants until my chest is clearer.

A day again spent visiting the afflicted households, although I fear I am not of the least service to the people amongst whom I am placed. Must I be an actor on a stage to communicate with them? Is the word of God not enough? I fear that too many have become accustomed to the Methodist manner. Yet that is not the sole reason for some enquire as to when the Reverend Harding will return.

I can at least be of some practical use. Oranges and wine are gratefully received. Mrs Heywood has braised some rabbits and to her I direct the families of those whom I feel to be in need of some strengthening sustenance. I can do little for those at Edge Mill however for they are not lacking in material goods but are nevertheless grievously afflicted. Jane Molland does not sit with her sick children for fear of passing the infection to the child she suckles. Her sister in law held the children in turn at the window while she waved to them and wept below in the yard, greatly sorrowed that she was not able to put her arms around them herself.

Tuesday 14th February 1871.

I cannot think that any in this village have sent Valentine's Day greetings.

Arthur Molland died today, aged 21 months. I was with him at the end as was Mr Allen, the Methodist minister, and I think our sentiments were much in accord. Arthur was a fine boy with round rosy limbs and curly brown locks. His passing was mercifully swift. I saw for the first time that this fever is a lesson to *me* in submission to God's will. I struggle to be equal to the trial.

I sense a change in the village. The fear of the fever is now so great that the support the cottagers traditionally offer one another is being withheld as every contact is seen as being of the utmost danger. I am frequently asked as to the welfare of a friend or neighbour for they no longer dare to visit if they have children of their own, except to close family members when they seem unable to keep away. Enquiries and news are sometimes called out from garden to garden or across rutted lanes but closer conversations are sadly missed. Fear and isolation are felt everywhere. The stench of disinfectant is in many homes. Twice I have been refused admittance because "us can't take the risk, zur." That is no surprise for I cough and sneeze and do not look the picture of health. Again, early to bed.

<u>Wednesday 15th February 1871.</u>

I have not stirred out of doors today for the weather was cold and damp and not likely to benefit my chest, which is still very congested. Mrs Heywood ensured that I had sufficient logs to keep a good fire all day and was most kind in administering to my needs, bringing up hot drinks and sundry items at every opportunity. I took advantage of the time to compose a sermon on the subject of sudden death and the necessity of habitual preparation. Mrs Heywood procured a copy of the *Bideford Gazette* for me and I read of the capitulation of Paris.

<u>Thursday 16th February.</u>

I officiated at little Arthur Molland's funeral today. There were very few mourners and none from the immediate village for the fear of contact with a family wherein a death has occurred is now very great. The little procession did not come through the village but took the more direct way through the woods where, I am told, Arthur liked to play with his older brothers and sisters. There are others in the family who are still sick with the fever.

Mrs Heywood tells me she "does not like the look" of me, and seems most concerned for my welfare. I admitted to her that I did indeed feel weary. She has asked me to spend an evening with the family on Saturday, playing at cards. I may accept, for perhaps some time spent in company would raise my spirits.

<u>Friday 17th February 1871.</u>

I fear I have been desultory in my application to my duties. Until today I had not visited Mr and Mrs William Powe since Mary's death, being caught up with my own frailties and anxieties, and I now find that there is much to do. I pray that I might be guided towards the best action.

The weather has been most pleasant today, the sun shining and a light breeze stirring in the trees and as I set off on foot this morning, I longed to take a stroll in any direction but to the village. I called first to see Mrs Grace Hookaway knowing that she would be able to inform me of any new developments in the village. I find it, also, entertaining to enter her little shop and see her tiny bowed figure almost hidden amongst the extraordinary jumble of goods she has for sale; flour, tea, bacon and sugar muddled together with soap, garden forks and jars of sweets on the shelves, counter and indeed on the floor itself.

As usual we retired to the back room and a warm hearth for a cup of tea. She has news of every family in the village, for not only do all visit the shop from time to time, she also visits those in need, having no children in the household to whom the infection might be passed on her return home. I believe that she also takes goods to many without thought for immediate payment. It was for Mr and Mrs Powe that she was most troubled, a concern I found to be justified when I visited them myself. She told me that in addition to Mr Powe's continuing grievous illness from which he appears increasingly unlikely to make a recovery, and the evident anguish caused by their daughters' deaths, the family are in serious financial difficulties such as will need drastic remedies to ameliorate. It is a month since either parent carried out any paid work. During the last three weeks the Friendly Society of which Mr Powe is a member have paid him bed pay of ten shillings a week, although this was reduced to walking pay of six shillings a week for a time, when it was found that he was able to leave his bed to attend his daughter's funeral. The Society has also taken care of the doctor's bills, but not the cost of the funerals. There is no pay for Mrs Powe as she is not ill. However she refuses to leave her remaining family to carry out any paid work and seems quite disinterested in the dire financial straits into which the family has fallen. The rent has not been paid for over a month and there is no money for the basic necessities of life; the family subsist on the gifts of ready-cooked dishes left on the doorstep by neighbours. Mrs Powe spends all her time sitting at her husband's bedside and the house is cold and dirty despite young William's efforts to keep things in order, for without his mother's encouragement he is easily disheartened. Mrs Hookaway was clear that the situation could not continue, but was at a loss to know what the remedy could be and sighed frequently in her distress at the sad case.

It was with some trepidation that I finally knocked at Mr and Mrs Powe's door. Young William answered and called to his mother who descended the stairs a few moments later. The house was indeed in a sorry state, exceedingly cold, the floor unswept and muddy, the table adorned with unwashed dishes. Both Mrs Powe and her son appeared unkempt. My questions elicited few useful responses; to my enquiry as to the health of her husband she replied,

"'tis hopeless zur, 'e's cast down and wored out".

Indeed she appeared so herself. I put it to her that she and her family no longer had the means to remain in the cottage and were in need of more care than she could herself furnish; the best course, I suggested, was to apply to the Guardians for admittance to the Union Workhouse. I genuinely considered this the most beneficial procedure to ameliorate the condition in which the family was placed. My thoughts were of aid and alleviation; I certainly did not wish any suffering on the family. I was, therefore, greatly shaken at her response. All signs of fatigue and melancholy vanished like darkness fleeing from a flash of lightning; her whole being seemed diffused with a terrible energy and her voice quite shocked me with its piercing tones. Her words rang in my ears long after she had run back up the stairs and they accompanied me in my somewhat stupefied walk back home.

I do not now know what to do for the best. It is obvious that any action that results in the breaking up of the remaining members of the family will be met with the utmost resistance. It is, I suppose, comprehensible that Mrs Powe should feel this way. Yet if they remain in the cottage with the rent unpaid they will, eventually, be evicted on to the street and will be forced to apply to the Workhouse in even more adverse circumstances. It is not certain that Mr Powe will live to see that day, yet with more careful nursing than his wife is able, in her distressed state, to give him, it may be that he would live. I know it is my duty to help this family in distress and I struggle to find the best course of action. I pray that the Lord might help me to see the way.

Saturday 18th February 1871.

I slept but poorly last night. Mrs Powe's voice resounded through my dreams and I awoke in the small hours to wonder whether I shall ever in this lifetime experience such love or such loss. When I was young I imagined that marriage, if not love, would one day be part of my life, but now I fear it may be too late. Such thoughts induced a most melancholic state of mind.

I visited some half a dozen households this afternoon, having returned home precipitously yesterday without completing my calls. I spent some considerable time praying with Mrs Jane Molland at Edge Mill. She sobbed piteously throughout and was quite unable at times to join in the responses. Indeed even my voice faltered once or twice. She has lost two children and another, a girl of nearly three years, is gravely ill. The mother's trial is all the more acute as a result of her having to keep a distance from the sick children in order to avoid passing the infection to the babe that she suckles. Elsewhere there are many who are now commencing their recovery from the fever but who remain weak and would be most susceptible should a further infection occur, as happened in the case of Mary Powe. Thus it remains of paramount importance that contact between families should continue to be minimal, a stricture that many find hard to bear and spirits are low throughout the community.

After very heavy rain and winds of the utmost ferocity overnight, the day was calm and bright. As I walked home from the village I stopped and leant upon a gate to admire the view down across the radiant fields to the rushing river in the valley below. Everywhere was the trickle of running water, the very earth wheezed with moisture and atop every blade of grass was a glistening jewel of dew lit by a dazzling, blinding sun hanging low in the west. The bare contorted fingers of the hedgerow trees reached out against a sky of perfect blue; at their roots a robin hopped and fluttered, murmuring a subdued winter song. I felt it wrong that I should be alive to see such wonders when so many of my neighbours have died, then jolted myself away from such pagan thoughts, for *they* are in the better place. Of a sudden I became aware that I was being observed by two labourers, who had broken off their work clearing a ditch further down the field to observe me, and I found I was leaning my head in my hands in a gesture of despondency. Both raised their caps on realising I had seen them and I turned hurriedly back to the road.

Nearer to Littleham Court a plaintive voice called out to me and I saw young John Williams from the farm cottage standing inside a field gate.

"Please maister, can 'ee tell us what time it is?" he enquired. When I replied, after consulting my pocket watch, that it was a little after four o'clock he asked whether it would soon be dark. He had been in the field since before first light, armed with a stick and a tin can, which he beat at intervals to keep the crows and flocks of sparrows from the corn. His thick heavy boots, made for feet much larger than his, were so caked with clods of earth that it was a wonder he could drag himself around the field. He earned, he informed me, fourpence a day, which is little enough but no doubt a valuable addition to the family's income.

I was glad this evening to join Mr and Mrs Heywood downstairs for supper, conversation and to play at cards. Their sitting room was warm and most comfortable and I felt quite at home. We were joined by Mr and Mrs Lewis Dennis of West Furlong Farm, Mr Caleb Friendship of Frithelstock, who is engaged to be married to Miss Elizabeth Heywood, and the four youngest in the Heywood family who are now aged between fifteen and twenty three years. We had a good supper of cold meats with pickles and potato pie, with fruit pies and cream to follow, and the company was lively and most informal during the playing of cards. It is curious how the Methodists, while most intolerant of music or dancing, have no aversion to card-playing provided, of course, that no money is exchanged. For myself, I do not think it to be a pastime I would wish to indulge in regularly, but it provided a welcome diversion this evening.

<u>Sunday 19th February 1871.</u>

I administered the sacrament this morning. I was glad to see both Mr and Mrs Alexander Dennis present and I understand that Mr Dennis is again playing a full part in the work of the forge. It is a salutary lesson that such a seemingly strong and intelligent man can be so brought to his knees by the loss of a little child, and a timely reminder of the power of prayer which has so aided his recovery.

As I rode back through the village, I noticed Dr Ackland's horse outside Mr and Mrs Powe's cottage and I await any further news. Their predicament continues to exercise my mind. I feel the best course would be their removal to the house of some respectable widow who might care for them until such time as Mr Powe is restored to health, if that be God's will, and they can again be independent. Mrs Heywood has suggested two such persons in the village who I might approach. Such an action would have the benefit of relieving the pressures on the family while allowing them to remain together. I know the Reverend Harding would be willing, for a time, to make up any financial shortfall which might occur after the weekly payments from the Society.

A good luncheon of roast beef, and cold meats this evening.

<u>Monday 20th February 1871.</u>

I was shocked today to learn that Mr William Powe has now contracted meningitis, a disease which is likely to prove most serious in his weakened condition. I met with Dr Ackland while walking this afternoon and he reined in his horse to inform me of the news. He is most gentlemanly in his demeanour and a reassuring presence when compared to some I have known. There was one whose manners were almost coarse and who was more akin to a butcher than a man of medicine. It seems that the malady is one that not uncommonly follows other infections, involves fever, visual disturbances and fits, and frequently results in death. My greatest fear is that it should spread beyond the confines of the cottage to the wider village. There are so many who are deficient in health and spirits that the effects could be severe. What am I to do? Should the family, after all, be taken to the Union Workhouse? It would be most beneficial if this area had the advantage of a hospital where those such as William Powe could be cared for in safety, without the shame and sorrow that so many associate with the workhouse. The doctor did not suggest a course of action and I confess I was so confounded by the news that he had ridden off before I could formulate any questions; he does in any case have many other pressing concerns to occupy him. I have spent much of the evening in prayer and in reading the Scriptures but I confess I am no nearer in finding a solution. I long to discuss the matter with a gentleman of intelligence and sympathy. It is at times such as these that I miss the Reverend Harding most keenly.

<u>Tuesday 21st February 1871.</u>

It has been a day of action and arrangements after which I feel quite fatigued. I pray that the course I have taken is the correct one.

When Mrs Heywood informed me at the breakfast table that there is the utmost fear in the village of the latest infection, with none prepared even to pass the Powe's cottage, preferring instead to pass at a distance through the field behind or along the lane that leads to the brewery, I concluded that removal from the village was essential. Mrs Heywood informed me of a house in Bideford at which I might enquire and I asked for my horse to be saddled at once.

The house at which I called is no.7, Richmond Terrace in Meddon Street and is the home of Mrs Sarah Lake, an elderly mason's widow who has had some experience of nursing the sick. She is a respectable woman with a pleasant enough manner, her every sentence accompanied by a curtsey as she assured me that she would look after the family as if they were her own. The house is clean and warm and the remuneration she requires is not very great. I returned to Littleham by the road that passes Upcott Mill, so that I could call at the Powe's cottage without retracing my steps. I informed Mrs Powe that a wagon would call in the morning to carry her family to Bideford and told her to prepare their personal possessions. She seemed somewhat bemused but promised to do as I asked; she was, I think, relieved that they were not to be conveyed to the workhouse and can therefore remain together as a family. I did not enter the cottage. It will, of course, have to be thoroughly fumigated before being re-let. I find my spirits somewhat lighter having reached a satisfactory decision.

Before leaving Bideford, I visited the Pannier Market as it has been some time since I have had occasion to visit the town on one of the market days of Tuesday or Saturday. I did not make any purchases but amused myself by strolling along the aisles and admiring the displays of wholesome foods. It was a scene not only of great commerce but also of social intercourse, for many matrons bring their daughters for instruction in the art and practice of purchasing and they in turn attract many bachelors from the town. I confess I would not have perceived what was taking place, had not Mrs Heywood, who was present, drawn my attention to the goings-on which she felt did not assist business operations. In the town I made some more purchases of blankets and foodstuffs to distribute among needy families.

Bacon and potatoes for dinner.


Wednesday 22nd February 1871.

I have been sitting here in my darkened room for over an hour before realising that a candle was necessary. I believe I have acted very foolishly. I intended no harm but I shudder now to think of the possible outcome of my actions and the public shame that could be incurred.

Having visited the Reverend Farringdon at Landcross this afternoon, I returned to my rooms and, being seated, picked up a copy of the Bideford Weekly Gazette from my table which was a week old and almost unread, owing to the fact that I have not had the leisure for reading newspapers. When I reached the back page and started to peruse the local news, I discovered an article concerning a fever hospital in Hart Street in Bideford. It seems that this "hospital" is merely a private house run by a woman who takes in a few fever cases from outside the immediate area for pecuniary benefit. I quote:

"it is a subject for general complaint that people, while suffering from infectious diseases, should be brought from an infected district to a thickly-populated and non-infected one, where their presence is likely to spread disease and death among the inhabitants of the locality."

Is this not precisely what I myself have done in the case of William Powe? I admit I did not consider those in the proximate area but merely wanted to rid the village of the danger. I have indeed been foolish and shortsighted and I fear the public castigation that would follow, should the matter become commonly known.

Little Ellen Molland, aged two and three quarter years, died today from the scarlet fever. God rest her soul.

My mind returns constantly to my own witlessness. Yet what should I have done for the best? I pray for forgiveness, and "cast all my care upon Him."

# CHAPTER SIX

As I studied the census returns for 1871 I found the names of the old farms in Littleham that still resonate in the village today: Langdon, Furlong, Boundstone, Dunn, Shutta, Heale and Apps. Many are no longer farms as the land has been sold off, the old farmhouses modernised and the barns sold and converted to luxury homes. Others have survived by buying up their neighbours' land as it becomes available making them far bigger than they were in the nineteenth century, for with today's reliance on machinery small farms are no longer viable.

There were fifteen farms in Littleham in 1871. The largest included Littleham Court at 150 acres, the nearby 145-acre Knowle Farm, Yeo at 182 acres and Higher Boundstone's 100 acres, yet even these are small by today's standards. Many other farms in Littleham were hardly larger than one of today's fields, from which hedges have been removed to make them workable by tractors of elephantine proportions. There was West Furlong, 40 acres; Lower Langdon, 30 acres; East Furlong, 20 acres; Lower Boundstone, 80 acres; Nethercleve, 28 acres; Hole Farm, now more attractively named Robin Hill, 50 acres; Lower Dunn, 70 acres; South Heal, 40 acres. In some of these farms the animals have gone, the yards are now gardens, the barns demolished or converted to garages or holiday cottages, the land sold off piecemeal.

Farms are often seen as symbols of tradition and continuity; it is imagined that they have remained in the same family for many generations and the changes that the last twenty years have brought are regretted. It is common to see the present as in a state of constant flux but the past as a golden age of stability. It would be easy to assume that the snapshot of a community that is provided by the census on one particular day is a long-term picture; however, comparing the 1871 census with those of earlier and later decades suggested otherwise. I found that, in Littleham at least, there had been many changes in the nineteenth century, not least with regard to the farms in the village. Shutta Farm for example, the building now converted to the village pub and its farmyard to the pub car park, was occupied by two families of agricultural labourers at the time of the 1861 census. It was uninhabited on the day of the census in 1871 and possibly for longer. By 1881 George Bale, described as "Butcher Farmer of 100 acres employing 2 men and 2 boys" was living there. Any additional changes that took place between these years are not, of course, recorded.

The acreage of farms changed from decade to decade as farmers took on extra fields or gave up land to their neighbours; this could be achieved with relative ease as the majority of farms were rented. Today many farms throughout England are owned by those who work the land, a change that came about largely after the increase in death duties in 1909. Many large estates were subject to large tax bills on the death of the landowner and were forced to sell off some of their farms in order to pay them; tenant farmers were then usually given the option to buy at a fair price. Before land ownership amongst farmers was so common there was far greater movement between farms. During the nineteenth century most farmers in the southwest leased farms on seven, 14 or 21 year leases and had no security beyond the term of the lease; this was in contrast to earlier centuries when farms were let for three lifetimes or 99 years. As a result, farmers often moved every few years as the landlord or need dictated and farms were not seen as family farms holding memories stretching back through the generations. In most cases however the move was to another farm within the parish, perhaps previously held by a relative or old friend so the history of the land was well known. In the census of 1841, eight year old

Lewis Dennis was living with his parents and eight brothers and sisters at Higher Langdon Farm. The family was still there in 1851, farming 165 acres, and Lewis's brother Alexander was living nearby and working as a labourer. By 1861 Alexander had moved into Higher Langdon and was using the outbuildings as a blacksmith's shop. Lewis Dennis had married and was farming 35 acres a mile away at West Furlong. He was still there in 1871, having increased his land to 40 acres and produced eight children, all of whom survived the scarlet fever epidemic. In 1881 he had moved to Adjavin, a farm of 180 acres two miles from Littleham and the census described him as "Employing His Children As Unders" - he had nine by then. The 1851 census lists forty people by the name of Dennis who were born in Littleham, and that in a village of only four hundred inhabitants.

Change was apparent not only in the moves from farm to farm but also in the movement between being employed and employer. The distinction between farmer and farm labourer was not as clear-cut as today. Some labourers rented and worked land on their own account for a period of years before returning to work as paid labourers and it was not uncommon for a farmer's son to work as a paid labourer on another farm before renting a farm himself when he married. It was also possible for a labourer to rent land and become an employer himself. John Nickols first appeared in the census of 1851 at Lower Langdon, living with his father Arthur. Both were working as agricultural labourers. Ten years later John had married and was still working as a labourer. By 1871 however, now the father of three children, he was described as a "Farmer of 30 acres of Land." By 1881 he had moved to Gregory's Langdon and was farming 35 acres with his 19 year old son Albert. By 1901 Albert was living in Mount Pleasant and working as a horseman at Apps Brewery, no doubt caring for the huge dray horses which would have been used there, and John, now aged 79, was still living at "Langdon" as a farmer and employer with his son Harry. Harry is still remembered in the village today as farming 20 or 30 acres at

Lower Langdon in the early years of the century before he too moved to Mount Pleasant.

Despite the apparent movement through social groups that some workers achieved, the lives of most workers would undoubtedly have been structured by their economic positions. The landowners are not the subject of this book, and lived a life that was remote both in social and geographical terms from those in the village. The farmers and their labourers, however, were much closer socially and economically than they were in some areas where farms were bigger. There would, however, have been very marked differences in standards of living between the farmers of 100 acres or more, and the labourers who had large families to support on low wages.

Social arrangements for labourers varied according to their age and the locality of the farm. It was usual for young unmarried labourers or "farm servants" to live in at the farmhouse; these were usually teenage boys, although William Morrish at Lower Boundstone employed a ten year old boy, William Dunn, living in as a "Farm Servant Indoor". Some of these boys may have been apprenticed, being sons of poor labourers, illegitimate children or orphans who were the responsibility of the parish because their families could not afford to feed them. They would be fed and clothed by the farmer and lived either in the farmhouse or in a loft over a stable, eating in the kitchen as members of the family. All the farms in Littleham had one, two or even three boys living in. As farm boys grew up and married, accommodation within the farmhouse was no longer suitable and they then had to find a cottage to rent. Some farms, especially those outside the village, had cottages next to or near the farmhouse, which they let to their labourers for a nominal rent. These outlying farms housing 20 or 30 people formed small communities, much as they do today now that the barns have been converted to living accommodation. There were 21 people at Littleham Court and the farm cottages in 1871. In the main farmhouse were eight members of the farmer's family, two housemaids, a farmer's boy and the curate, James Andrew. In one cottage were the farm labourer William Williams and his family of five; in the other cottage his father-in-law - also a farm labourer – mother-in-law and a lodger.

I was puzzled by the mention in the census of two cottages at Littleham Court. There are several dwellings there today in addition to the farmhouse, but all had been converted from farm buildings and there was no clue as to where the cottages might have been. The 1889 map showed the dark silhouettes of the buildings that still stand there today; the main farmhouse, a barn and roundhouse now converted to two dwellings, and single storey buildings built on three sides of a yard and converted to three bungalows; there was no sign of the cottages. The 1841 map told a different story, however. The long low buildings around the yard were not yet there and instead there were a number of other buildings, including one by the roadside large enough for two cottages. I drove past Littleham Court on my way to Bideford several days a week, but I needed more than a fleeting glimpse. I knew that Mrs Dorothy Hill, née Heywood, whose son Richard still farmed the land at Littleham Court, lived in one of the properties there and that she was a distant relative of mine, though I had never really met her and was unsure of what the connection was. I telephoned her and she kindly invited me to visit.

It was a grey windy day in November. Apart from the occasional passing car, one is now unlikely to meet anyone when walking through the village and today was no exception, for the weather was not inviting to the few who were at home on this weekday morning. The only living thing I passed was a dog, his nose snuffling down in the grass and his tail up and waving. Littleham Court is about a mile from the centre of the village so I had time as I walked to think about the children of William Williams, the labourer who lived at Littleham Court Cottage. No doubt they often walked on this road on their way from school or after errands for their mother. Were they happy children? Were they often hungry? Farm labourers and their families did not have an easy life in the nineteenth century. When food was in short supply the father of the family was usually given priority over the children so that he had sufficient the village to Moorhead and would not be easy on an empty stomach. At the top I paused to catch my breath and looked down at the buildings which made up Littleham Court and at the yard that held not cows but cars, now that it is no longer a farm. A sudden gust of the damp drizzly wind tore the last beech leaves from the top of the high hedge and whirled them over my head. Winter was coming.

Mrs Hill welcomed me in, talking all the while, and we soon established that she knew my mother from years ago when my family ran Friendship's bakery and restaurant, which catered for farmers in Bideford Marketplace. She agreed that we were "cousins of some sort" and was able to produce a family tree which we pored over, together with my copy of the 1871 census showing the Heywoods who lived at Littleham Court at that time. We were soon able to work out our relationship. In 1871 the farm was run by William and Sarah Heywood who lived there with five of their nine children, the oldest of whom was Elizabeth at twenty-seven and the youngest, Albert, fifteen. Elizabeth, I now discovered, had later married Caleb Friendship, my great-grandfather. Her brother Albert was Dorothy Hill's grandfather. It was not until later that I thought to look at the very first page of the census where the name of the enumerator or census taker is given and realised with a shock that it was William Heywood. The handwriting that I had spent so many hours deciphering belonged to my great-great-grandfather.

Dorothy showed me the layout of the farmhouse and buildings, now converted to seven dwellings making it a small hamlet in its own right, and explained the extent of the land. We admired the view from her window that showed the sweep of land down to Jennett's valley and up again towards the outskirts of Bideford, and shared our anxiety at the insidious creeping spread of industrial estates on the skyline. She did not know of any cottages at the farm in earlier years but brought out some papers including an old sale brochure, the paper now worn and thin with edges crumbling into dust. It gave details of an auction sale. I studied the cover. "North Devon", it was headed. "Particulars and Conditions of Sale of an Important Freehold Manorial Estate, Situate about Two miles from the Town and Railway Station of Bideford, Five miles from Torrington, Nine from Barnstaple and Two and a half from the Coast, Distinguished as Littleham Court, And comprising the Farms known as 'Littleham Court', 'Knowle', 'Higher Dunn', 'Hole', 'North and South Furlongs', 'Nethercleave', 'Boundstone' and 'Holland', the whole containing 440 Acres with its Chief Rents and Privileges, and the Advowson of Littleham With the Rectory House and Glebe Lands of 94 Acres, and Tithe Rent Charges apportioned at £202 per Annum, Which will be Sold by Auction by Messrs. Norton, Trist, Watney & Co. At the Mart, Tokenhouse Yard, near the Bank of England, on Thursday August 8th, 1872, at Two O'Clock Precisely, in Two or Five Lots, By Direction of the High Court of Chancery."

Dorothy let me borrow the brochure so that I could make a copy of it. It contained detailed descriptions of all the farms for sale including numbers of rooms in the farmhouses, descriptions of outbuildings and names of fields; being written only a year after the time I was interested in, it helped me picture the village and surroundings. It also solved the puzzle of the cottages at Littleham Court. Along with the farmhouse, agricultural buildings, "Enclosures of Arable, Pasture and Woodland" and "Three Capital Thriving Young Orchards" was "a House Divided into Two Tenements for Labourers."

Later I discovered by chance the fate of the cottages. I was in the Local Studies library searching through old copies of the *Bideford Gazette* when I found the following entry for October 1877.

"Littleham.

Two Cottages Burnt Down.- Early on Saturday morning, a fire broke out in the parish of Littleham, in a cottage occupied by Mrs Morris, an old woman, which resulted in the burning of that and the adjoining cottage, occupied by John Wodecott." (Actually Westcott, - newspapers were no more accurate then than now.) "Mrs Morris had been ill for some time, and her daughter, who was staying with her, went to sleep, leaving the candle burning near the thatch. The thatch took fire, and both cottages were burnt down before any attempt could be made to save them. Wodecot, who is deaf and blind, was saved from being burnt to death by being pulled through a window."

Mrs Morris, or Morrish, was William William's mother-in-law who lived next door to him in 1871, and John Westcott was a boarder living with her and her husband, described in the 1871 census as "blind from birth" and in 1861 as "coal carrier altho' blind". He was a brother to William Westcott, carpenter, of Mount Pleasant. He had moved around the village, living with his parents at Holland in 1841, with a relative in Mount Pleasant in 1851 at which time he was described as a pauper, back at Holland boarding with the Morrishes in 1861 and then on to Littleham Court Cottage with them. It was by chance that I found out that he had achieved a degree of fame in the area. I was given a cutting from the *North Devon Journal-Herald* dated March 8th 1866, which read:

"Blind Johnny, of Littleham, the hero of one of Mr Capern's beautiful poems, and to whom Elihu Burritt alludes in his "Journey from London to Land's End," has received a small douceur from a Berkshire quaker, together with an allowance of 2lbs of bread per week; and on Friday last, when Johnny received the gift, the gentleman acting as almoner took him to have his portrait taken, in order that many of Johnnie's friends may possess a memento of that sunnie face that ne'er the sun beheld. Blind Johnny has a pittance of 2s a week from the parish, and now and then he gets an honest penny by fetching coals from Mr How's wharf, for his neighbours in Littleham. It was on one of these journeys that Elihu Burritt met him and heard the blind man's minstrelsy."

Any information on individuals, other than that provided by the census returns and parish registers, had been hard to find but here were three different sources of information for John Westcott, all by virtue of his blindness. It was not possible to search for one of the photographs that were taken – surely a rare event in Bideford at this time- for even if one should remain, it was likely to be in a family album with no name to identify it. The poem, however, I imagined would be easy to find.

"Mr Capern" was of course Edward Capern the Bideford postman poet whose round, for fifteen years, entailed a walk from Bideford to Buckland Brewer and back each day. He published four volumes of poetry between 1856 and 1870 which were generally well received and he was able to number Charles Dickens, Charles Kingsley and Lord Palmerston among his admirers. He was awarded a pension of £40 a year from the civil list for the publication of his patriotic poems, but most of his poems were somewhat artificial rural idylls. A search through all four volumes failed to produce any reference to Blind Johnny of Littleham although there were references to "lilac-scented Littleham" and one poem entitled "Song of the Littleham Hop-Pickers" in which the eponymous workers declare,

"A merry group we gambol down
To our bowers of green and gold."

Edward Capern was the Bideford correspondent for the *North Devon Journal* for some years and his poems were sometimes printed in the paper. Perhaps "Blind Johnny" would be found there. But despite reading the newspaper for every week for a year or two prior to the article of 1866, it was not to be found. I had come to a dead end with two out of the three sources, the remaining one was Elihu Burritt's "*Journey from London to Land's End*".

Mr Burritt was, I discovered, an American linguist and pacifist who came to England to study English farming methods and disseminate his humanitarian ideals. His book is long since put of print but I managed to track down a copy at the Westcountry Studies Library in Exeter. I found that the main focus of Chapter 11 was the time the author spent with Edward Capern, accompanying him on his round from Bideford to Buckland Brewer and describing in great detail the journey along the Yeo Valley with its visits to cottages and farmhouses. He praised the beauty of the surroundings and the liveliness and jollity of the people he met. Littleham was not mentioned by name – it is probable in any case that the postman's round did not include the centre of the village – but on their return journey to Bideford

"...a human object came into view which changed the spirit of the dream. A poor, thin old man came struggling up the long steep hill, apparently bent to the ground under a heavy burden. His knees knocked together as he walked, and his steps were short, weak and unsteady...He had half a hundredweight of coal in a sack, high up on his shoulders, almost saddled across his neck. The weight and position of his load bent him almost double, so that his face was quite invisible. This was his daily task; -to stagger up these long pebbly ascents with a sack of coal on his back, which he carried to a little hamlet on the summit. He received three ha'pennies, or three cents, for carrying this load three miles. He usually made two trips a day, sometimes three. Still he was cheerful, even contented and happy. He knew the poet's voice, who sprang out of the cart and shouted some pleasant words in the blind man's ear, asking him to sing one of his own songs...Without endeavouring to straighten himself, but with his face still bending to the ground under his load, he sang one of Capern's "entire" with a fine, mellow, musical voice, which he modulated beautifully, although it was doubtful if he could hear much of it himself. There he stood, turning up sideways a serene and sightless face, his neck and cheek begrimed with coal-dust moistened with the perspiration that hung in drops to his long, iron-gray beard, and thin hair...Such a serene, contented, peaceful face I never saw before."

John Westcott was fifty years old at this time, although

Elihu Burritt judged him to be "between sixty and seventy." He was still in Littlcham in 1881 aged sixty-seven, lodging at Groves Cross Cottage but disappeared from the Littleham records after this. There was no record of his burial in Littleham and I wondered what became of him. After a search his name appeared. He died in 1895 aged eighty-one in Bideford Workhouse, his care in old age no doubt proving too difficult for the relatives and friends who had cared for him in the village throughout his life. Might the workhouse have proved a less fearful prospect for one who could not hear or see its degradations?

Littleham Court was not the only farm that had lost its cottages in the years since 1871. Another was East Furlong. At the time of the outbreak of scarlet fever, there were three families living at East Furlong Cottages; Ann Violet, a widowed gloveress with two young sons; William Glover, a shoemaker, his wife Lucy and two baby daughters; and Mary Ann Walters, a widow and shopkeeper who also had two sons. It seemed that the dwellings were not needed for employees of the farm at that time. East Furlong Farmhouse still exists albeit rebuilt at the beginning of the twentieth century, but there are no cottages in the immediate vicinity, so I looked at old maps to try and find out where they were. Confusingly, there were between one and three dwellings named as East Furlong Cottages in different census years so it was difficult to know whether I was looking for a terrace or an individual cottage that was divided for multi-family occupation. The 1841 tithe map showed the outlines of buildings opposite the farm, which still exist in a modern form, and the long narrow outline of a building a short distance down the road where the chapel, built in 1878, and Chapel Cottage now stand. It seems possible that Chapel Cottage is one of the original East Furlong Cottages and that the others, perhaps in a dilapidated condition, were demolished to make way for the chapel. Certainly in the 1901 census, there is just one cottage listed, at that time still referred to as East Furlong Cottage.

Labourers who lived in a farm cottage were probably the most fortunate as they were assured of continuous employment and, being so close to the farmhouse, no doubt extra perks came their way in times of plenty. On the other hand their master was close enough to ensure they attended the church or chapel according to his wishes and perhaps to see that the children attended school even when there were babies to mind or chores for them to do at home. Other workers found their own cottages to rent and it is likely that at least some of these were not employed regularly on just one farm but found work as and where they could.

In 1871 there were thirty-nine males over twelve years of age in Littleham described as labourers, farm labourers or farm servants. This was out of a total male population of one hundred and thirty one and excludes the many farmers and farmers' sons who worked at least as hard as their employees. The wives and daughters of farmers and sometimes also of labourers had their own clearly defined roles in agriculture, usually working in the dairy and being responsible for hens and calves. It was also common for women to be employed during times when the need for labour was particularly high, as during the hay and potato harvests. When these groups are included one can see that a large proportion of the population was employed directly in agriculture.

As I write I hear a deep slow rumble outside which grows closer and louder until the windows vibrate and the room grows almost dark. The massive combine harvester which throbs and thunders outside in the narrow lane while a car is moved to make way for it, creates almost as much of a stir as the steam-powered traction engine would have done early in the twentieth century. Children run out in excitement and stare up at the driver perched so high above them and even those who grumble about the passage of farm vehicles through the village stand in awe of it. The combine harvester with its one driver will have completed its task in a fraction of the time it took an army of men to reap and bind a field of wheat, and as a result of such mechanisation, there are few in the village today employed in agriculture. In 1871 there were few mechanical aids and it was generally accepted that it took one day for four men to reap and one man to bind an acre of wheat. One wonders what they would have made of today's fields of thirty or forty acres. Even when the binding was finished the corn had to be stooked and left to dry in the field, then carried in on horse drawn wagons to the yard where a rick had to be built and thatched. Only threshing was done with the aid of mechanisation, completing a job in a few days that in the eighteenth century would have occupied many winter days. Even the threshing machines however needed ten men to keep them supplied with sheaves and to carry away the grain and straw.

Today the fields are empty of workers but for an occasional tractor, whereas all work on the farm in 1871 was labour intensive. Anyone walking along the stony high-banked lanes in the vicinity of the village would not have had to go far before one or more men working in the fields called out a greeting. They would perhaps lean on a gate to chat and have a rest from the wearying labour of hedge laying or ditching. If working with horses however, a shout and a wave, or a raised cap if the walker was of superior social standing would have sufficed so as not to disturb the horses' steady rhythm.

Agriculture was certainly the chief industry in the village in 1871, and many other trades were dependent on it. The census showed that there were three blacksmiths, two of which also employed one man. Alexander Dennis and Lewis Crocker were centrally placed in the village, the first being at Langdon and the second, as far as I could judge from cross-referencing between the censuses, in the property now known as the Old Forge. The third, Lewis's father Arscott Crocker was at Summerhill at the bottom of Scratchyface Lane, a mile distant from the village but able, therefore, to attract the trade from more outlying farms. All would have depended largely on the farmers for their work, making and mending ploughs shares, harrow tines, scythes, spades and shovels as well as shoeing horses. There were two butchers who would have been slaughtermen as well as dealers in meat. The two village millers were of course situated in the valley, utilising the River Yeo for their power at Littleham Mill and Edge Mill. James Molland, a miller and farmer, lived at Edge Mill with his wife and six children. Edge Mill is situated in a tucked away position off the Yeo Vale Road; Littleham Mill by contrast is on the road, which enabled it at one time in the nineteenth century to double as a public house known as the Yeo Vale Inn. The alcohol side of the business was brought to a close, according to a report in the *North Devon Journal* in 1860, due to licensing irregularities. In 1871 the miller was John Dunn who lived there with his wife and two young children. His employee John Short, described as a "miller's carter" lived in an adjoining dwelling.

The census does not tell us the details of the millers' trade but it is possible that both mills, in addition to grinding corn for local farmers, ground malt for the brewery trade. I had seen Apps Brewery listed in the 1871 census but this was not the first time I had heard of it. Most of the facts I was discovering seemed to have been long forgotten but the knowledge of Apps Brewery has continued to the present day, despite having been closed in the early years of the twentieth century. The earliest reference to the brewery I was able to find was in Kelly's Directory of 1856:

"A large quantity of hops are grown here." (Littleham). "They have hitherto been consumed by small brewers and others in the neighborhood; but a spirited landowner in the parish, having discovered a mineral spring, has established the Apps Brewery, in which the Littleham hop is largely used. This beer is singularly bright and sparkling, and has been pronounced by Mr. Herapath, the analytical chemist, as possessing valuable medicinal properties, and to be especially adapted for the use of invalids and others of weak digestion."

By the time of the census in 1861, there was a "brewer" at Apps, seven men in the village listed as working as "brewery labourers", two as "maltsters", and one "clerk". By the time of the 1871 census, fewer men were listed as working there, but it is possible that some described as "labourers" were in fact employed by the brewery. Certainly the brewery was still flourishing for the *North Devon Journal* carried an advertisement on 18th May 1871 for:

## "THE APPS BREWERY CO.'S FINE SPRING WATER TONIC ALES,

9s., 12s., & 13s. 6d. per Firkin; a Fresh Porter, 10s. 6d.
per Firkin; Bottled Ales and Stout, 3s., 3s. 6d.,
4s., 4s. 6d., 6s., and 7s. per dozen.
Dr. Andrew Ure and Professor Herapath highly recommended
the Apps Spring Water Ales, the water
containing Magnesian Salts and Carbonate of Iron, being
excellent properties for invalids and the robust."

The abundance of wells around Apps also enabled production of "Aerated waters: Soda, Seltzer, Lithia, Potass, Lemonade, Gingerade, Effervescing Lime Juice" as claimed in an advertisement a few years later. Production was high enough to warrant building a private road from the turning to Ashridge Barton down to New Road, this way being more level for the large brewery wagons than the steep lanes down to Upcott Mill and over Upcott Hill. According to Major W. Ascott in his *"Random Notes on Old Bideford and District"* (1953), a gate at the Ashridge end was kept locked to prevent members of the public from using the road. After the eventual closure of the brewery it became a public road and is still known locally as Wagon Road.

Apps Brewery experienced mixed fortunes, being subject to two fires, one confined to the cooperage in 1864 when a spark set light to the thatched roof, and another major fire in 1885. The very detailed description in the *Bideford Gazette* of this latter fire gives an indication of the extent of the brewery at this time.

"The brewery buildings formed two sides of a triangle, the longer side being composed of the engine house, with brewing apparatus above, and a series of stores and cellars, at the back of which ran the mineral water manufactory. The other side was occupied by cellars and stores, and by offices." Further paragraphs state that the engine house had three storeys, and arched cellars ran under the brewery. All the buildings mentioned were destroyed by the fire, leaving only "the malting houses and a few sheds, which were detached."

Despite the article claiming that "it is not likely that the amount of insurance will cover the loss", the business must have recovered because there were still nine men listed as brewery workers in the 1901 census; one clerk, two carters, one cellarman, one engine driver, two waggoners, a barrel washer and a horseman. By the time Kelly's Directory of Devon was published in 1906 however, the brewery had disappeared and Apps was listed as a farm.

Local knowledge of another building has survived to the present day. The house now known as Hoop Cottage was, I had been told, originally the Hoop Inn. This was confirmed in the 1871 census, and the landlord's name, James Crealock, lives on in the name of the present pub, the Crealock Arms. The earliest record of the Hoop Inn that I was able to find was in the first census in 1841 and it closed in the 1920's. It was presumably supplied with beer from Apps Brewery but there did not seem to be any evidence that the two were more closely connected.

It is likely that the Hoop Inn provided solace for some of those whose families were affected by scarlet fever, as well as being a centre for social contact and information. Richard Jefferies, in an essay first published in 1874, wrote:

"The alehouse forms no inconsiderable part of the labourer's life. Here he learns the news of the day; the local papers are always to be found at the public house, and if he cannot read himself he hears the news from those who can. In the winter he finds heat and light, too often lacking at home; at all times he finds amusement; and who can blame him for seizing what little pleasure lies in his way?"

However he also warned:

"The alehouse is the terrible bane of the labourer. If he can keep clear of that, he is clean, tidy and respectable; but if he once falls into drinking habits, good-bye to all hopes of his rising in his occupation."

It is probable that the influence of the chapel in Littleham prevented drunkenness in many families but there was still sufficient trade in the village for the Hoop Inn to remain open throughout the nineteenth century, and for other public houses to open. None of the censuses of the nineteenth century listed other pubs and the first indication of their existence was from articles on Littleham from the *North Devon Journal*. As already mentioned the Yeo Vale Inn was closed down in 1860, but there was another pub in Littleham around the same time. The earliest mention of the New Inn was in Kelly's Directory 1856 where Eliza Harris was listed as the beer retailer and maltster. By 1865 William Mugford was the landlord, for in an article in the *North Devon Journal* entitled "A Publican in Trouble" it was reported that he had kept "open his house during prohibited hours on Sunday" and that "the constables had repeatedly complained of the disorderly way in which the house was kept." The article went on:

"The Chairman said he had no business to have men in the house at that time. -Defendant: Well, sir, they would come in and sit down; how could I help it? ... - The Bench fined the Defendant £5 and 10s. costs. – Defendant: What time will you give me to pay the money? – Chairman: No time at all. – Defendant: Well, I haven't got £5, and you can't get a shirt off a naked man, that's certain. (Laughter)"

As to where the New Inn was situated and whether repeated fines eventually led to its closure, this will only be discovered if further information comes to light, for its landlords are not listed in the census nor the building named on maps.

It was while studying the maps that I noticed the area beyond the church. I frequently walked through the churchyard to pass through the gate on the far side and out into a lane which leads up to the village hall in one direction and down across a field to a woodland walk in the other. The lane was familiar enough from my walks but an unusual aspect to it was noticeable on the map. On the 1889 map a short section of it was shown clearly, but the upper part, which leads now to the road and the village hall, was marked merely with a dotted line to indicate a footpath. On the 1841 tithe map the lower part of the lane was clearly marked but came to an abrupt end with no extension to the site of the village hall. I set off to scrutinise an area I considered I knew as well as my own back garden, but whose origins I had never considered.

Landscape history is a complex study and the story of the possible evolution of one village would be worthy of a book in its own right. However a quick glance at a large-scale map of Littleham suggests a few possibilities. The outlying position of the church immediately throws up some questions. It may be that the parish originally consisted of scattered farmsteads without the focus of a village centre, but nevertheless the position of the church is unusual, being remote even from the majority of the farms. It would seem likely that the village was originally centred close to the church, or that there were at least some houses nearby. Many villages have shifted over the centuries as dilapidated cob and thatch cottages sank into disuse and were rebuilt elsewhere, - to be followed by the dwellings of friends and relatives. The study of the landscape can often provide clues as to where previous dwellings may have been. I stood in the lane to the east of Littleham church, on the far side from the present village. The lane is sunk deep below the level of the fields that border it, a sure sign that feet, hooves and wheels have worn it away over many centuries. This lane now leads up to the village hall, built in the early years of the twentieth century, but the upper part is little more than a track and clearly of a much later date, being on a level with the fields and edged only by a wire and bramble hedge. The evidence provided by the maps confirmed this.

I looked around me at the high primrose-studded banks.

What would I have seen if I had stood here two or three hundred years ago? From the churchyard on the other side of the thick impenetrable hedge I heard young girlish voices singing in unison of love and loss, a sweet high sound made all the more charming by the slightly off key nature of one voice. Despite the exaggerated line breaks to enable swift intakes of breath and the drawn out American vowels carefully imitated from the girl pop bands they no doubt admired, the voices of the unseen girls had an ethereal, timeless quality. As I walked along the lane they, unknowingly, led the way on the other side of the hedge until they broke off as suddenly as they had started and turned instead to exchanged confidences as I passed on my way. Later I realised I was humming the tune quietly to myself.

On my left between two old oaks there was an old well half-hidden among a profusion of ivy and pennywort. I had always known it was there but had never wondered why. Perhaps the old lane originally ended at a cluster of cottages. The lower lane curves to the right towards the Rectory and into what is now a private property; to either side are areas of lightly wooded "waste" ground which undoubtedly had a purpose at one time. Hidden among a profusion of brambles and nettles was another well. An old long-used lane leading nowhere, wells supplying no one, surely there were once houses here? The area alongside the lane is large enough to have held several cottages and the lower part which now disappears into what were the grounds of the Rectory may have led to further dwellings. An old document relating to the church stated:

"1805 July: The old Parsonage house was taken down and the foundation stone of the new building laid by the Revd Nicholas Mill, and completely built and finished in Sept 1806."

It was not uncommon for unsightly cottages to be demolished in order to enlarge the grounds or improve the aspect of a large house; could it be that this happened in Littleham when the imposing new Rectory was built? It may be that this area once was the centre of the village but a detailed study, perhaps using aerial photographs, would be necessary to provide further evidence.

# Sunday 19th March 1871.

The morning sun is warm on William Westcott's back as he leans his weight on to his right foot and drives the spade into the dark earth. In one easy movement he lifts the soil, tips it into the trench and positions the spade for the next thrust, one spit deeper. In this manner he works steadily across his garden, the rhythmic movements soothing and emptying his mind. Throughout the winter this plot, a quarter of the entire garden, has furnished the family with fine green cabbages, the last of which was picked this morning and is now washed and chopped in the kitchen, ready for Sunday dinner. The spring cabbages are nearly ready, and the sun will bring them on. He reaches the end of the plot and straightens up, glancing down towards the unseeing windows of his empty house. Turning quickly away, he swings the spade on to his shoulder and strides to the top of the garden where the dung heap, produce of the pigsty and privy, is stacked against the end wall of the sty. Ignoring the view across the sweeping expanse of sunlit pasture beyond the hedge and the pair of buzzards that wheel and mew overhead, he digs steadily until the hessian sack at his feet is half full. He then carries it down the garden and shakes the contents into the trench, moving along sideways as he does so in order to distribute the clean dry manure evenly along its length. Immediately on reaching the end he takes up the spade and digs another trench, tipping the soil on to the manure to fill the first. He digs automatically and without pleasure. Around him sing all the joyful voices of spring: from the bare branches of a hawthorn the rich throaty song of a blackbird; from the depths of the hedge the rustle of active new growth and the busy movements and subdued squeaks of tiny creatures; and above, the flutter and excited chatter of blue tits, great tits and wrens as they prepare for the renewal of life. He feels wooden, devoid of emotion or any purpose beyond the immediate task. He knows that his brows have gathered into a frown.

When he reaches the end of the trench he stops to view his work and takes a rag from inside his waistcoat to wipe his face. The sun is extraordinarily warm for March and the air close and sultry. He looks up at the scattered black thunderclouds that only serve to intensify the brilliance of the sun; except for them the sky is a perfect azure and he knows that it will not rain today. Caroline, his eldest daughter, will have a dry walk. He feels his scowl diminish a little as he thinks of her. She has not been home since Mary Ann died.

The familiar rhythmic ring of boot nails hitting steel and the accompanying sigh of turned soil reaches him from a neighbouring garden and he walks over to the high, thick hedge over which dog-roses and convolvulus will climb later in the summer. George Britton's head bobs into view as he straightens from his digging and William shouts out a greeting, "All right then?"

The two men stand in companionable silence for almost a minute, staring at the narrow garden that lies between them. It is not cultivated as well as either of their own; groundsel and dandelions are pushing up between some dishevelled leeks, the broccoli has blown over and none of the ground has been dug this year. It belongs to two glove-makers, - an elderly widow and her unmarried daughter who has two children.

"Us had best get some taters in for 'er, eh George?"

"I do have some leeky seeds over, so I'll till they for 'er later when I've dug my own."

"'Tis 'ansum weather for tilling. 'Twill all be early, 's long as us don't get a late frost."

They gaze in silence for a few more moments then George Britton recommences his digging. William stands with thumbs thrust into his waistcoat and surveys his own garden. There is still a small stand of leeks; they must be pulled in the next week or two before any more go to seed. The purple broccoli will last a few more weeks. There are still two strings of onions and a sack of potatoes in the shed. Before long the two apple trees and the plum will be in blossom. He feels a familiar glow of pride at having seen his family through another winter. They live well. He always sees to it that Maria has something to put in the pot. In the sheltered beds near the house the first pea shoots are showing bright green against the dark earth, under fluttering threads from Maria's sewing box which keep away the birds. Beside them, marked with sticks, he has planted the first rows of carrots and next winter's leeks. He walks down the garden path to stare at the finely raked soil but it is only a week since he planted the seed; perhaps after today's warmth the seedlings will show. Again he grows aware of the silent emptiness of the house. He turns on his heel and walks with lowered head to the pigsty at the end of the garden.

The pig - a new acquisition and only a couple of months old - is stretched out on the straw as if prostrated by the unaccustomed warmth of the day. William takes a stick, kept propped against the wall for the purpose, and starts to scratch the pig rhythmically on the back. Its pink-lashed eyes blink with surprise and its hide twitches against the stick until the increasingly familiar tones of the man whispering soothing pleasantries enable it to relax again. After a while it begins to grunt with satisfaction. Even in two weeks it has put on weight. William always experiences a mixture of disappointment and anticipation at the purchase of a new pig. It is never as clever or affectionate as the last, yet there is an excitement associated with the presence of a new young animal. It is much the same as a new baby really.

William withdraws the stick and leans on the low roof of the sty. The grass is beginning to grow in the meadow beyond; it will not be long before it is again starred with buttercups, daisies and red clover. Both he and Maria had known since Mary Ann was a baby that she was not a normal child. She did not suck strongly and they thought they would never raise her. He knew some said, though not to his face, that it would have been better if she hadn't lived. He has never felt that, even now, but he wonders sometimes what Maria is feeling. Now that the anxieties that gathered about Mary Ann's future are gone, he should feel unburdened. How often had he worried about a time when she was too heavy, or he too old, to carry her downstairs? Although they had never expected her to live long, how many times had he lain awake fearful lest he and Maria were taken first, for who would care for Mary Ann then? She knew them and loved them, he knows that with a fierce conviction even though she could not put her arms around them or say their names.

With a start he remembers the meat roasting over the fire. He is used to breaking away from his work at regular intervals while the family are at church to see that Mary Ann is still comfortable on the bed on the floor ("If 'tis on the floor, there be nowhere to fall" Maria said most days to justify what seemed to her a meanness of provision) and has not trapped her arm uncomfortably under her body. The dinner had always been a secondary concern. He bids farewell to the pig and walks reluctantly down the path to the empty house. As he enters he feels his accustomed greeting, "All right then, chiel?" on his lips and he tightens them into a grimace. The room is still. He pauses in the low doorway. The well-scrubbed table is laid ready for seven, the flowers the younger children have given their mother for Mothering Sunday already in jars along its length. Maria has found a small ink pot for the primroses four year old Harry had given her, for despite the exhortations of his older sisters to "pick 'em long", there is only one inch of stem below each pale open face. The sun streams through the window, illuminating the now empty floor where Mary Ann used to lie, yet he still seems to see her. Can it be no more than a week ago that she was there? William turns to the fireplace and bastes the meat, throws another log on to the fire. Although he knows it is too early for Caroline or William to arrive, he goes out to lean on his gatepost. The sun is even hotter here and he pushes his hat back on his head. Across the lane wild daffodils cluster under the hedgebank elms, shaking their heads in the warm breeze. William watches as a hedge sparrow creeps and flits among them, uttering a gentle, melodious song that belies its mundane appearance. He used to show such things to Mary Ann as he cradled her in his arms and walked her up and down the lane and she would crow her open-mouthed laugh and try to fix her wandering gaze on his face. Again he longs for Caroline, his second oldest daughter who loved Mary Ann and brought her little presents when she returned from Yeo Vale House, - a ribbon for her hair or a sweetmeat from the kitchen which would have to be mashed in a spoon.

The excited voices of children drift up the hill towards him and a family rounds the corner, followed closely by another. The service at the little chapel opposite Higher Shutta has finished and the families, some reunited for the first time since Christmas Day, are returning home for dinner. He remembers the excitement he used to feel as a boy on Mothering Sunday, a day that stood apart form the normal run of things. He remembers walking home from the woods carrying the carefully gathered primroses and burying his nose in their soft faces and sweet heady scent; the delight and pride in giving a gift, and the almost girlish pleasure of his normally stern, harassed mother; the anticipation of dinner for which there was always something special, a good leg of pork, long-salted for the purpose, or perhaps a piece of beef.

Mr and Mrs Morrish from Lower Boundstone draw level with his gate and he removes his hat in greeting. Their children, all with highly polished boots and the girls with ribbons in their hair, subdue their dancing and chattering a little and he forces a little levity into his voice, feeling almost embarrassed at their awareness of his sorrow.

"Bootiful day innit! You could almost believe that it had been ordained."

"Couldn't be better, could it!" Mrs Morrish answers.

201

"Your older ones be coming home, bain't they? They'll be a comfort to you both."

She speaks sympathetically with meaningful glances to show that she is aware of his loss and William shifts uncomfortably. Mr Morrish, a thickset farmer with a broad, placid face who looks uncomfortably restrained in his Sunday suit, comes to the rescue.

"And how's the pig?"

The pig had, as usual, come from one of Mr Morrish's litters. William relaxes a little.

"'E's settled in proper now and 'e's starting to look for his mash."

The conversation, which could have continued at some length as there was still the neighbours' pigs, last year's pigs, and the merits and drawbacks of different breeds of pig to discuss, is broken short by the necessity of greeting Mr and Mrs Short, also returning from chapel. They are closely followed by James Middleton from Knowle, carrying his baby daughter Ellen whom he has just collected from Mrs Lucy Glover. Lucy has been feeding and caring for Ellen since the baby's mother died from the scarlet fever before Christmas. James cradles Ellen in one arm and carries a basket containing a cake for his mother, who lives a few doors away from William in Mount Pleasant. A slim young man with an open expression, he strides cheerfully along with a "'Tis almost like summer!" in greeting. Things are easier when you are young, thinks William. He'll find another wife quick enough to take the place of the last. He's still got his whole life in front of him. There will be more children.

The Piper children come straggling up the lane from the opposite direction, dropping as many primroses as they carry. One little girl of five or six is dripping water and grey mud from her misshapen frock.

"Her falled in the pond!" a bigger girl explains.

"You should watch out for her. Her could drown quick as a flash in that pond," William warns.

"No, her floats 'cos Mam says her's a little witch," comes

the complacent reply.

William watches them pass down the lane and into their house, their bare feet seemingly as tough as the stones on which they walk. None of *them* have succumbed to the fever. It is strange, he thinks, that those who are least cared for sometimes seem to thrive the best, at least after they have survived infancy. Maria has been washing the children all over twice a week with coal tar soap ever since the fever began and still Harry caught it. Thank the Lord he was soon over it. And Mary Ann ... they always expected her to be lost to an infection but in the end it wasn't that at all. The fits had got worse it was true, stronger and more frequent. Dr Ackland had said that was what had taken her away. But just finding her like that in the morning ... he'd never dreamt such a thing would happen. It was something he would never forget.

He cannot feel glad of the holiday today and he knows that despite the cheerful voices, all in the village feel the same. Now, three weeks since the last scarlet fever death in the village - poor little Ellen Molland down at Edge Mill - people are beginning to feel safe enough to stop and talk to their neighbours, but it is with a wary sense of security, for all know that the disease could return. All, too, have been touched by death in some way, some immersed in grief through the loss of those most precious to them, others sharing in the sorrow of the loss of so many young lives from one small community. The gifts of small posies of flowers are particularly welcome to those who receive them on this Mothering Sunday, but in other households the bare tables and the empty chairs that surround them are almost unendurable. How can Mrs Molland feel, having lost three of her six children? And Mrs Powe? First her three daughters - three! - and then her husband. William sighs and props his chin in his hands. Will the village ever be back to normal?

The relief at being out in the open air comes almost as a shock to Caroline. To be able to gaze at distant hills and gently wavering leaves instead of close walls and the hard surfaces of knives and wooden tables, to hear the rustle of grass and the murmuring of birds instead of shouted orders, these perceptions induce an acute pleasure that she cannot put into words but can only express in a sigh which is almost a groan. She turns and leans on the field gate to look back at the house, delighting in the freedom to stop when she wants, to do nothing when she chooses. The sun is warm on her back. She unfastens the top button of her dress where it bites into her neck and eases her hair a little from its tightly pinned confinement. The scent of wild garlic drifts up from where it lies crushed beneath her black laced boots. She runs her hands over the rough wood of the gate's top bar. It is strange to be looking at the outside of the house, to stand back and see it as others see it instead of being part of its busy, ordered interior. It makes her think sometimes of the ants' nests she used to uncover in the garden at home so she could watch all the ants scurrying along corridors with invisible walls, turning left here, right there, busy with their ordained tasks and oblivious of her gazing down at them. Caroline stares at the silent facade of Yeo Vale Mansion, which gives no indication of the industry within. Although she has worked there for several years, she rarely sees the front but knows every inch of the kitchen and servants' quarters at the back. The main entrance is set in a strange tower that always makes her wonder if it was once a church. The rows of windows on either side - thank the Lord she no longer has to clean them! - give the house a look of permanent surprise.

She thought she would never escape from the kitchen this morning. Mrs Archdall had been quite kind when she had curtsied and asked whether she might go home for Mothering Sunday as usual and the cook, Mrs Acland, had accepted the fact quite readily at the time - but this morning was another matter. This is the problem with being the only kitchen maid. Although she has plenty of opportunity to gain experience with the plainer cooking, it does mean that Mrs Acland finds it difficult to manage without her. Ann, the scullery maid, has been persuaded to stay on to help dish up lunch as she goes home to her mother every night anyway, but Mrs Acland still kept giving Caroline "just one more job before you go." Nevertheless the novelty of being released after only - Caroline counts on her fingers - five hours instead of her usual sixteen or so is wondrous. All the other servants, except the footman William Yeo who is walking home to Putford, live at far too great a distance to visit their mothers.

Caroline runs over the morning in her mind, happy to do this now she is away from the kitchen. As usual she had been downstairs by six o'clock to clean and light the kitchen range, fill the kettles and lay the kitchen table with everything Mrs Acland would need for preparing the breakfast. Then she got breakfast for the children and started on the baking. After that she was only supposed to have stayed long enough to start off the lunch but Mrs Acland had wanted her to help in the scullery so Ann would be finished early, then to start preparing the mayonnaise of fish for tonight's dinner and then, just when she thought she was ready to go, make a fruit cream. At least Mrs Acland had not shouted. Probably she knew she was asking too much.

Caroline takes a deep breath and turns back to the road that leads to Littleham. She can leave all that behind her now. It feels now as if she has been confined in that kitchen for a month rather than just over a week. Things change so quickly at this time of the year. There is a green haze on the bare branches of the hedgerow trees; the wild daffodils have opened, as have the first white flowers of the garlic. She stops and leans into the hedge to bury her nose in the soft yellow throats of the daffodils, inhaling their delicate sweet scent. She will pick some for her mother when she is nearer home. She pushes herself up and eases the waistband of her dress. Working in the kitchen has thickened her waist, and she always was on the plump side. "A praper ol' dumpling" her father calls her when he gives her a hug. She smiles at the thought of seeing him again. He is probably at home at this moment and looking out for her, though he will pretend to be busily engaged with some task or other when he sees her coming up the road, will say "'z 'at you already, maid?" as if in surprise when she calls out a greeting.

Now that she is walking at a steadier pace, she realises just how hot it is. Her chemise is beginning to stick to her back. And she is hungry, for breakfast was hours ago. Her mouth waters when she thinks of the lunch that she knows her mother will have prepared. With a start she remembers that home is going to be different. Whenever she goes home the first thing she does after embracing her mother and father and Thomas, catching Alice and Harry as they throw themselves at her in excitement, is to turn to Mary Ann's bed on the floor. She calls her sister's name and holds her head still to help her focus her gaze, waits for the chortle and the open-mouthed grin. But Mary Ann is no longer there. How is it possible? She can hardly believe it is true. When she is away she expects everything at home to continue as before and is surprised if her mother has moved a picture or stitched a new rug. How can such a change as this have taken place? She swallows hard to chase away the lump in her throat. She has not cried yet. Even when she lay alone in her hard narrow bed in Yeo Vale Mansion she did not cry, but lay staring at the ceiling, unable to believe that Mary Ann was not in her usual place.

The ringing clatter of trotting horses reaches her and a carriage drawn by two matched bays rounds the corner ahead. She recognises it as belonging to the lady and gentleman from South Yeo who often visit Captain and Mrs Archdall at Yeo Vale. She hurriedly steps sideways into the hedge to avoid the cloud of dust thrown up by the wheels and makes her curtsey as best she can in such an awkward position. The shadowy figures inside the carriage do not appear to see her.

Just above the turning to Buckland Brewer, three small children are playing with an old buckled wheel outside the farmhouse, bowling it along the road and running to catch it, shouting to each other all the while in shrill voices. The youngest, a toddler, falls and picks himself up again to totter on without a murmur. She can still hear them as she reaches Yeo Bridge and stops for a rest, leaning over the parapet to watch the water flowing beneath her. The river here is wide and shallow, winding its way gently towards the Torridge around islands of stones that in wetter spring times are submerged under rushing torrents. Beyond the riverside elms stretches a field of hops, grown for Apps Brewery in the village. The stone feels warm through the harsh cloth of her sleeves and the heat is becoming more oppressive. She turns and leans back on the bridge. But for the children's voices, it is very quiet. She imagines her mother in church, her forehead pressed against the cool, hard wood of the pew as she kneels in silent prayer, her tears under tight control. Caroline both dreads and longs for the moment when they can put their arms around each other.

From the opposite direction comes the sound of more tuneful voices and Caroline turns to see two young girls in pinafores and aprons walking arm in arm towards the bridge, singing a hymn in sweet high voices. So intent are they on negotiating the multisyllabic words and rapid changes in pitch that they seem quite oblivious of their surroundings and pass by with just a small smile of acknowledgement from one. The familiar rousing tune lifts Caroline spirits somewhat and she continues her walk, humming quietly to herself.

The hill that winds up past Furlong Farm is a steep one and soon, finding the heat trying and herself out of breath, she pauses to start making a posy for her mother. The primrose leaves deep in the hedge bank are large and lush and will look pretty encircling the flowers. She moves slowly, picking a flower here and a flower there, choosing those with the longest stems and the most recently opened buds so that they will last as long as possible. She intersperses the primroses with buds of wild daffodils and dog violets, carefully arranging them the way she has seen Mrs Archdall do with the large blooms from the glass houses.

A voice calls her name and she sees George Glover arm in arm with Mary, the housemaid from Higher Langdon, walking swiftly up the hill towards her. They exchange news of their respective journeys. George is walking Mary back to the village then returning home with his brother William, *his* wife Lucy and their children, for the whole family are to eat dinner together. They continue walking, George and Mary matching their pace to Caroline's slower one. Caroline notices how George caresses Mary's hand as it rests on his arm, how his eyes dart frequently to her face, hoping to meet hers in a glance of silent communication. She sees that George is quite the man, no longer the young boy she remembers from school and she feels suddenly the burden of her 22 years. As they push on up the hill there is silence but for the steady rhythm of their breathing and the melodious echoing call of a song thrush from a hedgerow tree ahead.

"I be sorry 'bout your sister, Caroline". Caroline can hear that Mary has been summoning the courage to speak. She feels the tears that have been so long coming beginning to build up.

"'Ave 'ee seed my mam? Do 'ee know how her is?" As she speaks, Caroline realises how worried she has been about her mother, knowing that she will not give in to sorrow easily, but will soldier on as sensibly and efficiently as ever.

"I 'an't seed her but I yeard as her was doing well." The lane levels out and their pace increases a little. "Mrs Powe, her's in a *terrible* state though and 'cos of her being in Bideford, folks can't help like they would if her was here. They say since Mr Powe died her won't let William out of the room for fear of losing him and her's nearly mad with sorrow. Mr Andrew be *tryin'* to help her but her won't listen to no prayers."

Mary seems almost to relish the news and Caroline again feels the gap between their ages. George's furrowed brow suggests a more sensitive nature, but Caroline inwardly excuses Mary's excitement, remembering that she has not grown up in the village and is not so close to the people who have been touched with such sorrow. She turns to him.

"Be Lucy's children well?" Lucy is a link between them, being mother to George's two adored nieces, and Caroline's best friend ever since they had walked hand in hand to school at the age of four.

"Oh they'm strong! Harriet, her never stops chattering, her's a praper little toad. And Lucy's still caring for the Prouse baby, but her's with her father today."

"Is it over now, the fever, do 'ee think?"

George considers. "'Tis three weeks now since the last one. There won't be no more now."

They pass the Hoop Inn and climb the hill to Crossways, pausing in the hot sunshine for Caroline to regain her breath and to greet the elderly brother and sister, riding in a donkey cart and clutching posies of flowers just as they did as children, who are in the village to visit their aged mother. Now near the end of her walk, Caroline feels reluctant to face her parents and unleash the sorrow she senses they all keep locked inside. When they reach Lucy Glover's cottage at East Furlong, she announces that she will come in with George and Mary for a few moments.

The low front door opens directly into the main room of the cottage, which looks strangely empty without the usual fire burning in the big stone fireplace on this hot day. Lucy is sitting with Selena on her lap, tying a large bonnet on the baby's head while three-year-old Harriet crouches on the floor trying to pull on stiff leather boots. She jumps up as they enter and runs to them in her stockinged feet chanting "Unc' George, Unc' George" in excitement until George swings her up into his arms. Lucy looks up smiling but her face changes when she sees Caroline.

"Don't come in! Don't 'ee cross the threshold!"

Caroline steps back in shock when she sees the aggression in her friend's eyes and how she clutches Selena to her and shouts at Harriet to "Come here, now!"

"Be there fever at Yeo Vale? 'Ave 'ee touched any who be sufferin'?"

"No, no one." Caroline's voice wavers and she finds her hands are shaking. "There be nobody there as has had it. I haven't touched nobody. I haven't left the place these two weeks."

"Be 'ee certain?"

Caroline nods and struggles to control her voice. "But I'll go if 'ee want."

"No." Lucy sounds near to tears herself. "I be sorry maid. 'Tis always on my mind, how to keep them well." She gets up and gives Caroline a hug, whispering a condolence for her sister as she does so, and after a moment's hesitation, passes the baby to her to hold while she ties on her own bonnet. Her husband William clatters down the stairs and they all exchange news of those who are in the village visiting, those whose arrival is soon expected and the unfortunates who live too far from home to visit their mothers or mothers-in-law. The atmosphere is festive and Caroline realises that she is the only one present to have lost a close member of her family. Those who have escaped seem almost to want to celebrate, and would perhaps do so were it not for the awareness of those less fortunate.

She feels a twinge of envy at the domestic scene. When they were children she had been in a more secure position than Lucy, who had led a strange disconnected life with little contact with her mother. In fact Caroline's mother had acted almost as a substitute for her, advising the lone father, passing on clothes for Lucy and allowing her and her brother to stay the night in the cramped cottage when their father expected to be back late from market. Caroline had looked on Lucy almost as a sister. Now that Lucy has so much - a cottage to call her own, a handsome and good-natured husband, two healthy children - it seems a reversal of fortune.

At last the family is ready and they say their farewells, George and Mary turning down the hill with them, leaving Caroline to continue in the opposite direction. She is weary now and fears that she will break down when she sees her parents, perhaps increasing rather than lessening their sorrow.

She passes the yard at East Furlong Farm and sees it is empty and quiet, all the morning tasks being completed early in preparation for dinner. As she climbs the hill towards Mount Pleasant the heat and the silence combine to give the village an oppressive air and her pace slows still further. As she rounds the bend she sees her father, arms resting on the gatepost and hat pushed back on his head just the way she had known it would be. As she approaches the first cottage he turns his head. She knows what will happen next and she smiles to herself. He does not wave or call out a greeting but turns away to hide his emotion, pretending he has not seen her, and pulls an imaginary weed or two from the little strip of front garden. She quickens her pace, so glad to be home now, ready to call to him and see his feigned surprise and the pleasure that lights up his face, and to feel the fatherly embrace whose strength is a measure of his love for her.

# CHAPTER SEVEN

We like to imagine that villages were – and are – somehow divorced from social, political and technological change, their inhabitants sheltered from the dramatic developments that take place elsewhere in a more troubled, capricious world. When I first started taking an interest in Littleham as it was in 1871, I did not picture it in the economic and political context of nineteenth century England; it seemed rather a village out of time, the small changes and shifts of fortune ever present in the locality but divorced from the events of history books. It was strange to think that in the same year that children were dying from scarlet fever in Littleham, Stanley met Dr.Livingstone in Ujiji; the Royal Albert Hall opened in London; the Franco-Prussian war ended; trade unions were legalised; the F.A. Cup was established.

It is likely that the villagers knew very little of these events. In contrast to today, the media had little impact. In the nineteenth century many villages in Devon were geographically remote from the industrialisation which was rapidly altering the face of England, but the wave of change which was affecting the towns gradually spread outwards to affect rural areas. It is difficult to know how aware William Piper, Martha Powe and the other inhabitants of Littleham were of the wider world in which they lived, but certainly the local manifestations of national developments would have been obvious. William Piper would have been knowledgeable about the steam-drawn threshing machine that rumbled into the village even if he knew little of the new methods of mining that enabled a hundred million tons of coal to be mined annually. Martha would have known of the availability of cheap clothing in Bideford shops but would have had little knowledge of the power looms that had revolutionised the textile industry.

Did ordinary working people read newspapers? I imagined at first that the *Bideford Gazette* or the *North Devon Journal* would have found their way into very many households, as they did in my childhood and as they do today. However research suggested otherwise. The first consideration would have been cost. *The Bideford Weekly Gazette and Devon and Cornwall Advertiser*, as it was called in 1871, cost 1d. If considered as a percentage of an average wage, this is the equivalent of about £1.90 today, too much for those trying to feed large families on very low wages, so it is immediately obvious that the farm labourers would not have been buying newspapers. How many in the village would have been sufficiently literate to read them? The newspapers of the day used far more complex language than do their equivalents today, and the small dense print was not broken up by illustrations or large explanatory headlines. It is difficult to gauge levels of literacy, but there are some guidelines. In 1837 69% of bridegrooms and 55% of brides were able to sign the marriage register, the remainder indicating their presence with a carefully scratched cross; by 1900 97% could sign their name – but it is likely that many of these would still have struggled to read a newspaper. The Revised Code of 1862 required schools to carry out annual examinations for their pupils. After their years in the Infant class, which lasted from three to seven years of age, the children were expected to reach new Standards in reading, writing and arithmetic each year which ranged from Standard One to Standard Six. The Standard Six in reading consisted of reading a "Short ordinary paragraph in a newspaper or other modern narrative". However few children, at least in rural areas, ever reached this Standard as they had usually only attended school part-time, and the teaching they received was usually less than adequate as the unfortunate, often untrained, teacher frequently had to teach the whole age range from three to thirteen years in one class.

Despite these low levels of literacy some Sunday newspapers, such as Lloyds Weekly News and the News of the World, were produced as working class papers. Gruesome murders were reported at great length, but they also contained detailed political coverage with arguments that were complex by today's standards. The paper was often read aloud to a group by the one whose reading skills were sufficiently well developed. Nineteenth century newspapers were generally far more serious in their content than they are today. The 1819 Blasphemous and Seditious Libels Act prevented publication of sensational stories and it was only after its repeal in 1870, along with gradually improving levels of literacy, that a more popular press gradually developed. In 1896 Alfred Harmsworth founded the Daily Mail, costing ½d per issue, and promised his readers that

"...four leading articles, a page of Parliament, and columns of speeches will NOT be found".

Until the founding of a popular national press, it was unlikely that any in Littleham would have read national newspapers. An advert I found in an 1871 issue of the *Bideford Gazette* suggested that national newspapers were not commonly found in newsagents as they are today:

"DAILY NEWSPAPERS
All the London Daily Newspapers supplied after the arrival of the 3.50pm train daily. Terms on application to E. Honey, "Gazette Office", Bideford."

No doubt those who did read newspapers passed on news to their neighbours. If Edward Capern, the Bideford postman-poet is to be believed, the postman was often a carrier of news. In his poem "The Rural Postman" he wrote:

"The harvester, smiling, sees him pass,
'How goes the war?' quoth he;
And he stayeth his scythe in the corn or grass,
To learn what the news may be."

Advertisements for lost sheep, cottages to let and job vacancies were as common in local papers as they are today and it is probable that relevant information was passed on orally to those who were unable, through financial or educational constraints, to read the papers themselves. Whether news of a war in a distant country of which he knew little or nothing would have held much interest for a farm labourer is doubtful, unless he had relatives who were in the Forces. He did not have the questionable benefit of television and radio which brings the outside world into every home and it is, perhaps, hard for us to imagine his world view, constrained, as it was, by lack of availability of travel, books, and the media. As he struggled to produce the next meal for their children, it is likely that he would have had little idea of the powerful position Britain held in the world order.

In 1871 Britain was by far the richest country in the world, its wealth having increased rapidly throughout the 1850's and 60's. There was scarcely any competition as far as manufacture and commerce were concerned, Britain being responsible for one third of the world's trade in manufactured goods. There had been huge expansion in the iron and steel industries to produce the materials for railways and shipbuilding and for the manufacture of machinery that was exported all over the world. Coal and the textile industry had also seen huge advances. Behind this unprecedented growth lay the discovery of gold in California and Australia, the extent of which led to great confidence on the part of the Bank of England. Credit was freely extended, allowing the formation of new companies and expansion of the old.

These developments were apparent at a local level in Bideford. The town had developed rapidly in the previous twenty-five years as a result of the railway, which was extended from Barnstaple to Bideford in 1855. This enabled further developments in trade and also the transportation of tourists who were interested to see the "little white town" described by Charles Kingsley in his book "Westward Ho!" which had been published in 1854. Hotels were opened and new houses built to accommodate the people attracted to the town from outlying areas by developing opportunities in trade and manufacturing. 1871 saw the opening of Bideford's first collar factory; two more were to follow and by 1895 a thousand people were employed in the industry.

The British Empire had expanded rapidly in Africa, China, North America and India. The imperial pavilions of the Great Exhibition of 1851, which were visited by six million people in one year, did much to foster pride in the Empire though it is unlikely that any but the most wealthy from the Bideford area attended, the railway not having reached Bideford by that time. Britain was in an immensely strong world position with a thriving economy; the desire to protect this at all costs frequently led to decisions based more on what could be achieved than on any moral considerations. Rebellions against British rule were sometimes met by brutal reprisals by British troops, as was the case in the Indian Mutiny of 1857. It was generally assumed that in the areas dominated by Britain, native people would prefer "civilised" practices to their own customs. These assumptions usually proved to be of benefit to Britain, for instance the teaching by missionaries in Africa that nakedness was ungodly led to greatly increased exports of British cottons to clothe the naked "savages". The raw materials were picked by African slaves in North America, imported by Britain for manufacture then exported as cloth to Africa.

Spending on defence was low throughout the middle years of the nineteenth century and was concentrated on protecting Britain's trade routes. The route to India lay through the Mediterranean and it was the desire to protect this route from possible Russian expansion that led to the outbreak of the Crimean War. Compromise and conciliation were rarely to be seen and there was little interest in the rights and wrongs of foreign disputes, even those concerning Britain's closest neighbours. Britain depended on shipping for the defence of its waters and its trade routes. Shipping increased rapidly and by the end of the century, Britain had more registered ships than the rest of the world combined. Bideford, however, had declined both as a port and as a centre for shipbuilding, although small sailing vessels still traded from Bideford to

Cornwall, Wales and Ireland.

This material prosperity and confidence led to a mood of complacency, which was apparent not only in foreign policy but also throughout the arts, philosophy and domestic policy. There was much emphasis on the virtues of industry and honesty, financial gain being seen as the inevitable reward. Unfortunately the poor were, by default, assumed to be lazy and dishonest and social policy did little to narrow the huge gap between rich and poor. It is unlikely that the poor people of Littleham would have regarded their poverty as unjust even if they knew that Britain was the wealthiest country in the world. Contemporary documents suggest that most people accepted the status quo; they did after all know no different. Popular novels of the time frequently featured heroes and heroines who had fallen on hard times but were able to "better themselves" through hard work, high moral values and respectability. Charles Dickens was one of the few to show a darker side of life that included pickpockets, child-beaters and early death. The attitude of arrogance and complacency, which we often see as the most typical and unattractive feature of the Victorian era, was really only widespread in the middle years of the nineteenth century and even during that time there were, of course, dissenters. Although religion played a very large part in Victorian life and was most often expressed in terms of conventional morality and spiritual apathy, there were some who were more radical in their beliefs. The Church and the bible-reading public were to receive a huge challenge during this time when Charles Darwin published "On the Origin of Species" in 1859. In the same year John Stuart Mill published his "Essay on Liberty" which questioned commonly held opinions of the nature of society. Elements of doubt and dissent were to grow throughout the middle years of the nineteenth century and in 1871 their strongest expressions were still to come.

Gladstone, the energetic and popular Liberal, was Prime Minister in 1871. It is likely that there was limited interest in political issues in Littleham. Only a tenth of the population was entitled to vote and all of these were, of course, male. Outside the towns, suffrage was limited to those who lived in houses rated at £12 or more, and owners of property worth at least £5 per year. This would have eliminated most inhabitants of the village. Even these numbers represented a huge increase on previous decades, however. As a result of the 1867 Second Parliamentary Reform Act the number of people entitled to vote was increased from one to two and a half million. As still more were enfranchised during coming years, so the ruling classes were motivated to improve conditions for the poor in order to attract their votes.

During Gladstone's first term, which lasted from 1868 until 1874, his government remodelled and simplified the legal system, the civil service and the military, improvements that included recruitment by ability rather than by influence. These changes enabled improvements to be made, over time, to social conditions, including increasing state responsibility for public health and a national education system.

The inhabitants of Littleham would, of course, have been well aware of their monarch. Queen Victoria had been on the throne for thirty-four years by 1871. She was not at this time a popular figure; having retreated into mourning when Prince Albert died in 1861 she did not appear in public for several years, refusing even to attend the State Opening of Parliament. The very high costs incurred nevertheless by her and her children led to hostile reactions in the press, which in turn did not endear her to the public.

Population was comparatively low in Britain in 1871 at just over 22 million; this was considerably less than either France or America. Since 1851 more people had been living in urban than in rural areas; it would be another thirty years before this was true of any other countries. By 1871 nearly four million people lived in London, making it by far the largest city in the Western world. It had not yet spread as far geographically as it has today but was far more densely populated and was a showcase not only for the greatest riches but also the most extreme poverty. It was a great lure to many from surrounding towns and villages. To a young man or woman the city offered not only financial rewards but also greater independence, the excitement of new experiences and much wider social opportunities than were available in the home village. People naturally moved to the large town or city that was nearest to them, so inhabitants of Littleham were more likely to move to Bideford, Barnstaple, Exeter or Bristol than to London, unless there was a specific social contact or offer of work. The move to urban areas was to accelerate later in the century when the decline in agriculture provided fewer opportunities for employment. Many village cottages were left to stand empty, a strange contrast to today when the desire to leave the cities causes the most dilapidated shed to be renovated and sold as a "barn conversion".

As more people moved into overpopulated cities so public health measures became necessary. Conditions in many parts of large towns and cities were appalling; grossly overcrowded with poor or non-existent sanitation, limited access to fresh water and a lack of affordable fresh food. Although housing conditions in rural areas were often very poor, at least most families had a small garden in which to grow fresh food, and unpolluted air. Throughout the century there was a growing awareness of the need for government to safeguard and improve the wellbeing of its people, a duty which embraced health, housing and education. Outbreaks of cholera emphasised the need for action, but progress was slow. The government had little authority to order local governments to take action on public health, and they often had little interest in doing so. This was partly for financial reasons; rates would have to be increased which in turn would cost votes. Conditions in areas such as Appledore, as highlighted in the *Bideford Gazette* in 1871, may seem appalling to us, but improvements in public health had been made – admittedly affecting towns more than rural areas – and far more would soon be under way. The Public Act of 1875 would order the appointment of medical officers of health in each area to supervise public health issues.

Despite the relatively low population, population growth was rapid throughout the nineteenth century, outstripping even the huge expansion in industrialisation. At the most basic level this meant that competition for jobs was fierce; if a man was unwilling to work the very long hours required of him, there was always someone else waiting behind him who would. The prospect of unemployment was regarded with foreboding, as, of course, it is today, especially by those thrust out of work after many years in the same trade. How much worse it must have been when there was a very real risk of one's children crying from hunger, or the family undergoing the shame and suffering of being separated and committed to the workhouse. The poor were expected to be independent, yet low wages meant this was frequently an impossibility. The gap was filled with the payment of "outdoor relief" to prevent the necessity of the whole family entering the workhouse, and with charity. There were charitable foundations providing schools, alms houses and regular sums of money to those who were able to meet set criteria; charities set up to provide for particular sectors of the population; and hardship funds to help those affected by severe winters or widespread loss of trade. There was also a huge number of middle and upper class individuals who were involved in charitable donation, classically the lady of the big house who visited cottagers and gave money or, more often, food, clothing and blankets. There was also a vast underclass in the nineteenth century who survived – or not – on begging, theft and prostitution. The farm labourers who endured exceedingly long hours for very low pay would have been well aware of how much worse their lot could be.

Work dominated people's lives to a greater extent even than today. With twelve-hour days being common, and all household chores taking many hours longer than they do today, there was no time for leisure in the lives of the poor. However, despite the enormous contrasts between the lives of the rich and the poor, the middle years of the nineteenth century were years of social stability and economic progress.

There was little overt discontent, unlike the earlier years when the Chartists and protestors against the Corn Laws were loud in their complaints, and the later years when the first trade unions were formed and the unemployed took to the streets in demonstration. The concept of self-help was fundamental during the years leading up to 1871. The labourer who could not afford to feed his children adequately despite working a 70 hour week was more likely to extend his vegetable plot and search for extra paid work to fit into a free hour in a summer's evening, than to expect help from the state or those wealthy enough to help him. Taxation was, in any case, so low that there was no money in the public purse to help any but the "deserving poor" who had shown that they had done all they could to remove themselves from their predicament.

Despite the long hours and low wages that many workers had to endure, conditions had been worse in the past. England was, in 1871, at the peak of a golden age in agriculture, growing almost all its own corn and having very little competition for any of its products. There had been many improvements leading to great prosperity, particularly on the big estates, but small farmers also thrived as high prices and cheap labour benefited all farmers. Many of the older people in Littleham would have remembered the hard times in the 1830's and 1840's when, partly due to the introduction of new machinery, unemployment was high and wages exceedingly low, leading to riots in some parts of the country. They did not yet know, in 1871, that agriculture was set to decline in the next few years, brought about by several disastrous harvests, the increased importation of cheap grain from America and Canada, and in 1880 the importation of the first refrigerated meat from Australia, New Zealand and South America. This decline was to affect the landowners, particularly those in wheat-growing areas, more than the labourers however. As more workers migrated to towns, so farm wages rose and this, coupled with lower food prices led in time to more comfortable living conditions.

There was always the chance of emigration for those who

wished to make a new start. Approximately three million people left Britain to live and work in the British colonies and America between 1850 and 1880, although the numbers decreased somewhat in the latter half of the period due to increased prosperity in England. Assisted emigration was available in some cases, board and passage being paid either for servants who agreed to work for an employer for a stipulated number of years, poor families for whom the parish preferred to make an individual payment rather than provide long-term support, or individuals who were awarded assistance by the Colonial Land and Emigration Office. Although ships were not sailing from Bideford to America in 1871, there were opportunities available for those who were considering emigration. The *Bideford Gazette* regularly carried advertisements:

"EMIGRATION

By Royal Mail Steamer to New York and Quebec three days a week – fare £6 6s. By sailing ship £4, Children up to 12 years £2.

For passages apply to H. Lee Hutchings, Auctioneer and Emigration Agent, 15 Mill Street, Bideford."

There was, of course, limited communication from those who had emigrated, as letters home had to be transported by sea which involved a slow journey with no certainty of eventual delivery, a marked contrast to today's emails and phone calls which provide instant reassurance and news. Nevertheless it is likely that many in Littleham had their vision of the world expanded by news of the new home of a friend or relative who had emigrated.

Travel from Littleham was, by necessity, on foot, or on horseback or cart for those sufficiently wealthy. The popularity of bicycle ownership was yet to come, the first all-metal bicycle having only been patented in 1870. There was no public transport from the village, a situation that has changed slowly for it is only in the last few years that the bus service has increased from one bus a week to two a day. Once in Bideford however, travellers had access to the rail network.

By 1870 there were 15,500 miles of track and every aspect of life was affected by this revolution in transport. If it was chiefly in the interests of industry that the railways were first put to work, passengers quickly saw the advantages of rail travel for journeys to work and increasingly for travel to the coast and countryside on days off. In 1871 the Bank Holiday Act enforced the concept of public holidays and many thousands crowded on to the trains to escape the towns and cities. It is likely that the railway affected Littleham in more prosaic ways as farmers carried their milk and vegetables in carts to Bideford Station for transportation, while for others the expansion of the railways provided opportunities for work. Domestic servants were able to travel further for work with greater ease, and by 1881 two million people were employed directly by the railways. The coming of the railway drove other forms of transport from Bideford out of business; by 1871 the last passengers were being taken by horse-drawn coach and a steam ship that had been carrying passengers to and from Bristol for many years was about to make its last run. Work on the railways was notoriously dangerous with serious accidents and deaths being commonplace. May 1871 was to see the death of a Littleham man working on the railway in London. Meanwhile the census in April listed six railway engineers, John Stormy born on the Isle of Wight, his three sons and two lodgers all living at East Heal Cottage, not far from where the railway line was being extended to Torrington, due to open in 1872.

Local events such as these would have made a far greater impression on the residents of Littleham than the doings of Parliament or distant wars. Nevertheless national and international developments affected every aspect of their lives, just as tides and storms on distant shores affect an island.

# Friday 7ᵗʰ April 1871.

Lucy Glover turns over in bed again and lies tense and still. Beside her, William's regular breathing falters and she puts a hand on his twitching shoulder to reassure him. He has managed an hour or two's sleep tonight; she - has she slept at all? She does not consider the restless, fretful dozing of the first half of the night to be sleep. His breathing calms again. She sits up carefully and slides her legs out of the warm bed. He does not stir. She feels the coarse rug beneath her feet, reaches for her clothes laid out on the chair. Selena snuffles a little in her cradle. She will not wake for an hour or two. Lucy holds her clothes under one arm so as to use two hands to open the latch silently, and tiptoes out on to the dark stairs. The door to the next room is ajar and she senses rather than sees that her mother-in-law is, as she had hoped, dozing in the chair. The small form in the bed, just visible in the candlelight, is still. There is a strong smell of disinfectant. For the last hour there has been a brief respite from the pitiful cries and beseeching sobs that leave Lucy shaking with anguish and helplessness. She strains her senses for reassurance until she hears a small sigh and sees the blankets moved by a shuddered breath then turns carefully down the steep, narrow staircase.

In the room below, the embers of the fire still glow faintly in the hearth. A few sticks, some carefully placed pieces of coal would soon revive it; but she does not wish to risk waking those sleeping above. She pulls her night-gown off over her head and dresses quickly and silently. She feels for her apron on the back of the chair and her shawl and bonnet from the hook on the scullery door. Yet still she must light a candle. The table where she sat and wrote her messages in the night is furthest from the fire and in total darkness. As the candle flickers into life she quickly gathers up the scraps of cloth from the table and pushes them into her apron pocket along with a reel of thread from her workbox. She replaces the pen and bottle of ink in the box high in the shadows on the mantle-shelf and turns to the door. With her hand on the latch she hesitates, staring at the floor. With a sudden decision she moves swiftly back across the room and takes Harriet's little china cup from the table and puts it in her pocket, then steals quickly up the stairs and into the chamber where her daughter and mother-in-law sleep. On the edge of the bed lies a small cloth doll, worn threadbare after much handling and forgotten for the last few days. Lucy hesitates for a moment then takes it gently and puts it in her pocket along with the cup and the pieces of white material and creeps back down the stairs and out through the door.

Once outside in the lane she stops, overcome for a moment by the unfamiliarity of being out in the village before even the horsemen at the farms have stirred, and by the strangeness of her task. Yesterday's showers have passed away and the wind has stilled. A late half moon illuminates a few scattered clouds in an otherwise ink-black sky, making visible the huddled silhouette of the unlit farmhouse ahead with its backdrop of trees, the ponderous body of hills beyond. In the stillness and the silence before dawn there is a sense of anticipation, as if something momentous is about to occur. It is a sense, almost, of hope. But this is Good Friday, the darkest day of the year, and Lucy knows that the worst has not yet come.

She remembers her mission and walks quickly up the lane. She shivers as she passes the first house in Mount Pleasant where Mrs Powe used to live. Three weeks ago she visited Martha Powe in the one small room in Bideford that she now shares with her son William. Just the two of them left out of a family of six. The visit had frightened her. Mrs Powe had huddled silent in the chair, her eyes like dead things.

"Can I get 'ee some supper?" Lucy had asked. Then "'Ave

'ee any tea to brew?"

As she searched on the shelf and tended the fire she had made herself talk of events in the village, choosing her words carefully; Mrs Vilot's argument with the pack woman over the extra pair of gloves; Henry's walk home in the storm. William sat close to his mother and stared at the floor.

"'Ave 'ee any taters?" Lucy asked, then after a search found a sack outside the door. Finally when she'd tidied the little room that was cramped with their possessions she put the boiled potatoes and bacon on the table and said,

"This is from our own pig. Did 'ee know, Mr Westcott has taken in your pig now? 'Ee'll bring 'ee some in when 'tis killed."

She should have thought. It must have been the reminder of her old life. Mrs Powe clung to William and cried as if her heart would burst, calling out the names of her husband and daughters, wailing so loud Lucy felt sure the neighbours would come running. The boy, crying himself, tried to comfort her but looked frightened and defenceless. Lucy had been unable to do anything to help and when Mrs Powe was quieter had made her farewells, hoping they would eat the food later. It had been a long cold walk home. That was before Harriet fell ill.

The cottages in Mount Pleasant crouch together in the darkness. A dim light shows in just one window where there is sickness in the house, but it has passed now from most dwellings. For a time, many people had believed that there would be no more deaths. Yet, to Lucy, it seems that the stench of disinfectant is everywhere, and the fear of disease and death hangs in the air, unseen, so that every breath is a hazard. If she could she would have left her cottage, taken her family and moved far away, out of the village. It is too late now.

She passes Mount Pleasant and turns down the hill past the hushed farmyards of Higher and Lower Boundstone, past the pond where the cattle drink. She hears a distant sound and pauses where a gateway allows a shadowy vista over fields sloping south-easterly to the valley and allows her eyes to adjust to what is not so much a lightness as a lack of total darkness. The sound comes again; it is faint as if coming from a great distance, a cry with a strange, open-ended quality like something searching, questioning, something unfinished. It is repeated, then again, and again, a voice from another world. She stands motionless. It seems as if time will not move forward while this sound continues. She believes for a moment that she can stand here forever in the darkness, with Harriet at home asleep in bed. The day need not come, bringing with it, perhaps, what she dreads the most. Then she shakes herself out of her reverie, turns quickly down the lane to the church. It is a fox barking, that is all.

The darkness in the deep lane is complete. The grotesquely contorted shapes of the trees silhouetted against the sky bear little resemblance to their comforting daytime appearance. She feels her eyes grow wide both with the effort of peering into the gloom, and with fear. It is silent but for the ring of her boots on the stony lane and the occasional rustle of a vole amongst the new growth in the hedgebank. It is many days since she has been out of the house. In her mind the last two weeks are a confusion of anxiety, days and nights running in to one another uncharted by the usual pattern of waking, eating, working, sleeping. They have been marked only by crises: the first heart-stopping realisation of Harriet's illness; the knowledge after a few days that the fever was severe and the doctor must be called; the agony of cutting off Harriet's beautiful hair. Lucy remembers the first soft down on her baby's head, how it had darkened and grown until it reached the three year old's shoulders, how she had brushed and curled it, how pretty it looked set off with a red ribbon on Sundays. She weeps now each time she sees the poor, bare head, shorn like that of one condemned. Yet she would have been glad of it if it had helped just a little to make her daughter better. Anything which would help. Even the leeches. Lucy shudders at the memory of the previous day. She wishes now she had not let it happen, for it had not helped. She would never, ever, forget Harriet's terror and suffering and the little hands trying so ineffectually to push the doctor away.

A tawny owl calls from the woods, a sudden sharp exclamation which makes Lucy freeze and her heart pound as surely as it would a mouse or vole. She draws her shawl more tightly across her and blinks back the tears that come so frequently now. She never used to be afraid in the dark. She came down here last week, late one evening after Dr Ackland had been. He had offered no hope, and while William sat with Harriet she had walked down this lane to the church. She sat in a pew near the back in the dark and asked the Lord to save Harriet. She realised then that she had never really prayed before, never really meant it the way she did now. She did not use any of the words she had been taught, or that special voice that Mr Andrew used, but just talked to God through her tears, told Him about her little daughter and how she and William loved her above all else. She remembers now how high her voice had sounded in the still, dark church, and how her pleas had echoed like those of a bird calling to its lost mate. She had thought then that someone was listening. She had not been afraid as she walked back in the dark.

She hears a sound that confuses her at first. It grows louder as she draws near and she recognises the tinkle of the stream where it runs through the culvert under the lane. Lucy and her brother Henry used to throw leaves and sticks into the water, watch as they vanished into the black hole before running across the lane to experience the magic of their carefree, dancing reappearance in the sunlit ripples on the other side. She is taken aback for a moment by the familiar sound of the stream, shocked that it should still run on such a night. It seems to belong to another world. She passes the shadowy presence of the old poor house and reaches the church gate. The latch is stiff and yields with a sudden click. The church looms massively above her against the gloomy sky. Beyond, the churchyard is hushed, enfolded in darkness, the soft contours of hillside and hedgebank just visible as they huddle around the church. She moves more quietly now, almost holding her breath and placing her feet gently to keep her footfalls silent. She passes the church porch, then the jewel-like colours of the stained glass window lit by the candle that always burns on the altar within. She hesitates for a moment, reluctant to leave the welcoming glow, then turns away into the darkness beyond the church. On the slope above her the dark bulk of the old yew tree is just visible against the sky, but beneath it the darkness is impenetrable. Then the moon reappears from behind a cloud, making visible the scattered congregation of headstones and the shadowy mounds of the new graves. She stops, overcome by the stillness and the silence. There is the grave of Sarah Middleton, mother of baby Ellen; there Sarah Dennis; here the three little Molland children, all taken in two weeks; there little William from Littleham Court, and Martha Powe's family, her husband, her three girls. Beyond in the darkness lie all the former inhabitants of the village, some she has known, and many who passed before her time. Nothing moves; not a leaf, not a blade of grass nor the smallest creature. The only sound is her own blood pulsing through her body, the only movement the rapid rise and fall of her breast. She thinks of the empty spaces they have left in the village; the bare pillows, the empty cradles, the vacant chairs around the table. How strange that they should instead lie here, in the cold and the stillness and the gloom. The sparse, white light of the moon gives the prospect before her a strange insubstantial air, like pictures on the old schoolroom wall seen in a dream. But she saw the burials. They were not a dream.

A cloud moves over the moon and the prospect fades from view. The cold is penetrating more deeply; Lucy can feel it biting into her bones and she huddles into her shawl as she moves towards the gate that leads out of the churchyard, holding out her hand in anticipation when she senses she is nearing it. She closes it behind her, shutting out the thought of the light in the church window, and turns left into the dark lane. The track here is little used and it is many years since any stones were put down to smooth the way. Once she almost slips on the mud. After that she reaches her foot out tentatively with each step, testing the ground for ruts and puddles. Looking down, the darkness is impenetrable and she fears she will wander off the track into a ditch, so she stares up at the sky and the silhouettes of the wayside trees that mark the way. Like this she feels her way forward, one step at a time and with arms outstretched, up the steep rough track.

Surely now the place must be near? How will she find it and how can she carry out her task when it is so dark? She stops to get her bearings. At first she can make no sense of the position of the trees against the sky and feels as lost as she would in an unfamiliar place. But there, ahead, the track curves up to the right. Here, just a little further on the left, stand the two old oaks. They mark the end of the old bank that divides the track from the churchyard. Between the oaks is the well.

Lucy is unsure why she has come on this mission. She knows no one who has done what she plans to do. But she has heard stories. Stories of magic wells, holy wells, wells that can heal, wells that can make wishes come true. She has forgotten the particulars; the visit should perhaps take place in the moonlight, or was it daybreak? Whether the person who was sick should be present, whether this was the right well - or had the stories come from another village altogether? She has no special reason for choosing this well rather than any of the numerous other wells around the village, except perhaps for its proximity to the church, and a half-forgotten memory of peering into its mysterious disused depths as a child. She does not know and does not ponder the answers to these questions.

She pulls her shawl more tightly around her and moves quickly up the track towards the oaks. Between them she can see the ivy-clad arch in the bank. Has the moon come out again? She looks up, then back towards the east. Greyness is spreading into the sky; daybreak is approaching. She stands in front of the well and hesitates. The ancient stone canopy is built into the high bank and the well itself is only a little higher than the track. Water is rarely drawn from it now although it is said that it never runs dry. The stonework is overgrown with the flat round leaves of pennywort and a tangle of entwining ivy. Water drips slowly from inside the stone arch and falls into the blackness with an echoing plop far below. Lucy takes a deep breath and sets about her work.

She starts by breaking twigs from the lower branches of the oak tree. Some snap easily, others are green and bend but will not break. When she has collected half a dozen she finds the reel of thread from her apron pocket and squats down in the lane with her materials in her lap. She takes two twigs and fashions them into a cross, securing them with a length of thread which she breaks with her teeth. When she has made three crosses she searches for more twigs, looking this time for dry fallen sticks on the verge, for the sky is growing lighter and the darkness in the lane less complete. When she has completed six crosses she reaches again into her apron pocket and pulls out the scraps of cloth that she had torn from Harriet's old petticoat. It is still too dark to read the words she wrote on them by candlelight but she looks at each one as she pushes the top of the cross through the threadbare material. Does this one read "Put here to let Harriet live"? And this "Pleese make her well"? As the sky grows lighter, she can just make out the words on the next, "Harriet Ann Glover. She is ownly 3." As she works she starts to cry. This one, she can see in the gathering light, is the little picture she drew of Harriet with a smiling face, this one "Make the fever go. Pleese." As Lucy gathers up the crosses and pushes them between the stones and into the turf around the well, she see the futility of what she is doing and starts to sob, her whole body shaken by her shuddering breaths. She sits back on her heels and gazes through her tears at the pathetic little flags that now decorate the well then hunches forward, her arms clasped tightly to try to still the paroxysms of sobbing. She must finish what she has come to do. Lucy stands up and takes Harriet's cup from her pocket. It is said that it is lucky to break china on Good Friday. She holds the smooth round shape in both hands, remembering how she had coaxed the hesitant little sips when Harriet was being weaned, then with a sudden movement smashes it hard against the stone lip of the well. Some pieces fall straight into the gaping mouth with a distant splash, the others she gathers up and throws quickly in. Next she takes Harriet's doll from her pocket. Ignoring the plaintive little voice that seems to cry in her head "Mama, no! No!" she drops the doll swiftly into the well and turns, running back down the track to the church gate. Once there she throws her arms around the gatepost and sobs uncontrollably.

When finally she can cry no more she dries her face on her apron and blows her nose on the inside hem of her skirt. She leans against the gatepost, too exhausted to feel anything anymore. In the upper branches of an oak tree a blackbird starts to sing. The first fluting notes only serve to emphasise the silence that floods back after they cease. It is a silence so complete that Lucy feels it must come from within herself, for it is more profound than any she has heard by day. Then the mellow voice breaks through again, just four questioning, experimental notes as if uncertain whether the greying sky is indeed harbinger of the dawn. She stands motionless, neither listening nor able to move. When finally the blackbird's song comes again, it is gaining in strength and resolving to celebrate the morning. For morning has indeed come, a grey light having spread throughout the sky and a thin drizzle starting to fall. Lucy turns and opens the gate. In the churchyard she sees the wild daffodils and primroses in flower where the ground has not been disturbed, their colours celebrating the coming warmth. How is it possible that they do not feel the enveloping mist of sorrow that has spread through the village? She walks on, her footfalls as insubstantial as the fine rain that drifts rather than falls on to her hair. The growing strength of the blackbird's melody is joined by a burst of song from a wren, which skulks in the moss at the base of an old gravestone and she turns to see its throat pulsing with the energy of its rejoicing. She passes the church, goes through the far gate and towards her home, although empty now of hope and drained even of sorrow.

The dark and colourless landscape through which she has walked is now appearing in a multitude of forms and hues as the sun emerges above the horizon. In the shadow of the hedgerow trees, wild daffodils, as bright as the sun itself and Harriet's favourite flowers hold their heads shyly away from the ponderous bumblebees emerging into the light. A song thrush exclaims its delight again and again, is joined by a chaffinch further up the lane, and then by more birds until the intervals of silence are gone and the air is filled with birdsong. On the bare branches of the blackthorn, the first flowers lie like a veil of late frost; the starry yellow and white flowers of celandine and stitchwort gaze up from beneath. With a sudden flurry of black feathers half a dozen rooks rise from the pines near the Rectory, their harsh discordant cries rending the sky. It seems they are the only creatures to convey a sense of disquiet; wherever else she looks she sees and hears expressions of joy, which deepen her estrangement from her surroundings. It is said that the sun dances as it rises if watched from the top of a high hill on Easter Sunday, just two days away; what will those days bring? From across the fields comes the mocking laugh of a green woodpecker. Lucy pulls her bonnet forward to shut out the light and walks quickly, with face downcast.

She reaches the edge of the village as it starts to wake. Sensing her approach, a young rabbit sits up on its haunches, its quivering ears almost transparent in the early light, before disappearing with a few rapid hops into the long grass of the verge. From Lower Boundstone a cock crows and a dog barks; there is the rattle of a bucket from the stables, smoke rising from a chimney in a thin column undisturbed by passing breezes. Lucy walks on as if through a dream. A door opens in a Mount Pleasant cottage after she has passed by and footsteps run after her; she turns only when Maria Westcott grasps her arm and presses a paper bag into her hand.

"Here, some cross buns for 'ee. They'm warm from the oven. Us is thinkin' of 'ee constant, maid."

Lucy takes the bag wordlessly and drifts on, leaving Mrs Westcott standing in the road, gazing after her. A dog on an early morning foray from the farm stops to watch her pass, snuffing the air to reassure itself of her substantiality, before continuing its way along the verge, nose down and tail up and waving. She passes on down the hill as if through another time, her form indistinct now in the misty morning light, a distant shadowy figure reaching a cottage door, and passing through. Then the click of a closing latch.

# CHAPTER EIGHT

The first death in Littleham from the scarlet fever epidemic that was already affecting the Bideford area was that of William Williams. He died, aged four years, on the 1st December 1870 and was buried in Littleham churchyard on the 3rd December. On his death certificate the cause of death was given as "Scarletina, malignant sore throat, certified." His father was a farm labourer, William Williams, and his mother was Maryanne Williams both of Lower Littleham Court, one of two farm cottages that lay just below the farm of the same name. He had four brothers and sisters, Ann aged eleven, John aged nine, Mary Jane, two, and Richard, seven months. Six years previously the family had lost another son, Henry, aged 14 months. No headstones remain to mark the graves of either of the boys and it is probable that the family were unable to afford them. The cottage where they lived has also disappeared, a piece of waste ground with an uneven surface which perhaps hides the outline of the dwelling is all that can now be seen.

While living at Littleham Court the family attended chapel, for I found the names of the younger children in the Bideford Circuit Wesleyan Register of Baptisms. The older children, Ann and John, had been baptised in the church, however. At that time the family had been living at Hollands, a mile away on the other side of the village. Perhaps their landlord and employer at that time had been a churchgoer, whereas their landlord in 1870, William Heywood, was a Wesleyan Methodist and it may be that the family was encouraged to fit in with his religious preferences.

After the death of little William Williams at the end of 1870 there was more tragedy ahead for the family. Maryanne died the following year, leaving the four remaining children motherless. No doubt Ann, then aged 12, took on responsibility for the younger children until her father William remarried, which he did a few years later. By the time of the 1881 census he was living with his new wife, Hannah, their four children aged between one month and four years, and his ten-year-old son, Richard, from his first marriage, who had been a young baby when little William Williams died. By the end of that year all the children were fatherless.

No one in Littleham would have been surprised by the death of four year old William Williams. Isolated child deaths from scarlet fever were common. The next death in the village was more unusual, however, and gave a warning of the severity of the fever that was spreading through the area. Knowle Farm lies at the end of a narrow track, just within the parish of Littleham and about half a mile from Littleham Court. In 1870 it was farmed by a 54 year old widow, Ann Prouse with the help of her son Thomas and an "indoor farm servant". Also living with her were her 19 year old daughter Sarah, Sarah's husband James Middleton, and their new baby daughter, Ellen. All the young people had been brought up in Littleham and James's parents still lived in Mount Pleasant. We cannot tell how many people in the household contracted scarlet fever; perhaps it was only Sarah. In any case she died on 30th December 1870, shortly before the new year that was to bring so much sadness to the village. The death certificate does not state how long she had been ill but if she had had the fever over the Christmas period her mother would have found it hard to keep her bedroom warm, for the weather in Britain was exceptionally cold. Francis Kilvert, the curate of Clyro near Hay-on-Wye, whose published diaries have become almost as well known as those of Samuel Pepys, wrote on Christmas Day 1870:

"It was an intense frost. I sat down in my bath upon a sheet of thick ice which broke in the middle into large pieces whilst sharp points and jagged edges stuck all around the sides of the tub like chevaux de frise, not particularly comforting to the naked thighs and loins, for the keen ice cut like broken glass. The ice water stung and scorched like fire. I had to collect the floating pieces of ice and pile them on a chair before I could use the sponge and then I had to thaw the sponge in my hands for it was a mass of ice."

When Sarah Middleton died her daughter Ellen was only three months old and still in need of her mother's milk. Patent baby bottles were available at this time but were very unhygienic in design and it is probable that more babies died from bacterial infections caught from dirty bottles than were saved by the milk in them; in country areas however it was still common to resort to wet nurses. Whatever method was used for Ellen, she thrived. I traced the family in the 1881 census and found James Middleton living in St Pancras, London with his now 10 year old daughter and his new wife. He was a "house decorator" and had perhaps been attracted to London by the abundance of work created by the acres of terraced houses that were being built.

The first two deaths took place on farms outside Littleham but by the time of Sarah Middleton's death, the fever had already moved into the village. There are no records to tell us how many people caught scarlet fever. The Register of Burials is a crude measure of the extent of the infection and we can only guess what percentage of the total it represents. Judging by reports of other outbreaks of scarlet fever in the nineteenth century, a death rate of one out of 20 of those who contracted the illness was considered high. In Littleham, from the entire population of those aged 16 and under, one child in 12 died. It is unlikely that every child in the village contracted the illness, so the death rate amongst those who did was exceptionally high. By the time the third death occurred, it is likely that the fever was affecting many others, particularly as the incubation period is only two to four days. The peak of mortality, however, was still to come.

The third victim was eight year old Sarah Dennis. She lived at Lower Langdon Cottages with her father Alexander aged 49, a blacksmith, and her mother Ann aged 48. She was the youngest child of six. Her two older brothers were no longer living at home but her two sisters, Ann aged 21 and Selena aged 17 were "gloveresses". She also had an 11 year old brother, John. It was difficult to work out exactly where the family lived. Lower Langdon Cottage was the first of five with that name in the census; there were also four houses called Langdon Cottages. In 1901, Alexander Dennis, now a widower aged 78 and a "retired blacksmith", was living at "Langdons Cottage" with his son John, also a blacksmith. It is likely that this was the house now known as the Old Forge, which is situated at a crossroads a short way above the houses that still bear the name of Langdon. There was a blacksmith called Dennis living and working there in recent living memory; if this *was* John I wonder how often he thought of his little sister Sarah who died on New Year's Eve 1870.

After Sarah's death there was a lull for three weeks. It may be that many children fell ill during this time and perhaps came close to death; or perhaps the disease seemed to abate, giving hope that it would not prove as serious as in other areas. But by the end of January any hopes would have been dashed and during the next few weeks the village saw more deaths in a short time than ever before in living memory.

Seven-year-old Elizabeth Powe fell ill with the fever on 17th January. Her father, William Powe, was the groom and butler at the Rectory and was 13 years younger than her mother, Martha. Elizabeth had two sisters and a brother. The family lived in Mount Pleasant but were not originally local to Littleham, William having been born in Peters Marland and Martha possibly in Bradworthy, but her records were hard to trace with certainty. William had been working at the Rectory for at least ten years but his wife and children did not join him in the village until later, perhaps waiting for a cottage to become available to rent.

The family had no relatives in the village to help them when they were stricken with illness but it would be safe to assume that their neighbours, living so close in the terrace of little cottages, did all they could to help. Help would have been needed for the disease was fast and devastating in its action. Elizabeth was the first to contract the fever and died on Saturday 21st January after four days of illness; five year old Ellen died on the following Wednesday; eleven year old Mary fell ill at the same time as Ellen, but lingered for three weeks. Three weeks after her death her father William died in Bideford, the three remaining members of the family having moved to lodge in Meddon Street after the death of the three girls. The death certificate does not state the length of time that William was ill, but does inform us that scarlet fever was followed by meningitis. By the time of the census on April 2nd Martha and her ten-year-old son William had been on their own for a month.

Many genealogists and local historians have been shocked by the discovery of multiple deaths within a family. Well-nourished in our safe, hygienic English homes we are cushioned from the harsh realities still experienced today by a majority of the world's population. The high child mortality rate of nineteenth century England is mirrored today in many Third World countries. In Africa many children are orphaned through AIDS. Whether they are separated from us by time or by distance is perhaps less important than our ability to empathise with their suffering, for it is that empathy which is central to our humanity. For a time the Powe family encapsulated that suffering for me. I thought a lot about Martha who had lost her husband and her three daughters in such a short time, and my awareness of her pain connected me with the many, many others who have suffered, and continue to suffer. My concern developed into a desire to know more about her.

It was difficult to work out which Mount Pleasant house the family might have lived in, as they did not appear there in either the 1861 or 1871 census. In April 1871, just a few weeks after they had moved to Bideford, there were no empty cottages so their home had already been re-let. In a cottage at one end of the terrace, probably Culver Cottage, was a miner called Thomas Marshall and his family. He might perhaps have worked at the paint mines in Bideford. He was a local man, having been born in Bideford, but must have lived away for some years since his children, including the youngest aged 14 months, had not been born in Devon. Clearly he was a relative newcomer to Littleham unlike most of the inhabitants of Mount Pleasant, many of whom had been present in the previous census returns, so it may be that he was living in the cottage previously occupied by the Powe family. Whichever house in Mount Pleasant they had inhabited, they left there after the deaths of the three girls. Who or what convinced Martha that she should move her husband, no doubt already ill by this time, away from the community that they had known for ten years to board with Sarah Lake, a 61 year old mason's widow in Meddon Street, Bideford? Was the decision purely financial and was Martha capable of making such a decision unaided at that traumatic time?

Historical records in the form of census returns and church registers can only give us the barest of facts. They can never tell us how an individual looked, how he adjusted to the life he was dealt, whether he smiled often or was of a gloomy nature. Perhaps because we can find out so little, the little we know takes on a significance beyond its true value. I had not been able to find out much about Martha Powe; even her maiden name remained as one out of a possible three that I had found. So when I tried to find out what had happened to her after the death of her family, my expectations were not high.

I searched for her and her son William in the local index to the 1881 census, ten years after the death of their family. This was before I had access to the CD which accomplished such searches in a few seconds; instead I sat in the North Devon Record Office poring over the typed index, making a note of all the references to the surnames Pow and Powe, for both had been used in relation to Martha. Then I obtained the microfiche of the 1881 census and started to search through the reference numbers I had written down. After a short while her name leapt out at me, Martha Powe, aged 54, lodger, widow. She was working as a stay-maker, probably making corsets for one of the drapers in town. Below her name was that of her son. William Powe, 20, lodger, joiner. So he had not become a groom like his father. A name further down the page caught my eye and I froze, unable to focus for a moment. Caleb and Elizabeth Friendship, living at 5a Honestone Lane, Bideford. My great grandparents. My eyes travelled up the page again. Martha was lodging at 5 Honestone Lane with Charles and Catherine Heywood, my great, great uncle and aunt. The names of their five children were partially familiar to me but the children at 5a: - I had not known them when they were young of course but as adults they had featured prominently in my childhood. Eda aged five, Lilly aged three, William, two, Alfred, eleven months. The memories of my great aunt Eda flooded back to me: a tiny little woman who never married; who spoke her mind even when her words were hurtful, but who would help anyone in trouble, usually by baking a cake; a familiar presence at the table for Sunday afternoon tea: - I could have *asked* her about Martha and had the thin facts of the official records fleshed out with memories and anecdote. But my sense of time was askew. Eda had died in her nineties when I was still a teenager, years before I lived in Littleham or knew anything of Martha Powe. I studied the pages of the census return again. My great grandparents had one servant living with them, Ann Williams, aged 20, and born in Littleham. This was the sister of William Williams who died at Littleham Court. What had seemed remote events, taking place not in the last century but the one before that, seemed suddenly to be catapulted into the present by the connections that were appearing before me.

It was not, of course, really so extraordinary. My great grandmother was born Elizabeth Heywood and lived at Littleham Court until her marriage. What could be more natural than she should choose as a servant the daughter of the labourer who had worked for her father for many years? And if there were rooms to let, why not let them to poor Martha

Powe and her son who had lost their family to the fever when living in Littleham some years ago? I had not originally known, however, that I had any family connection with the village and it had not been for family reasons that I had been drawn to research the gravestones that stood in the churchyard.

Martha Powe was not buried with the rest of her family in Littleham churchyard. I was unable to find any more records relating to her or, at first, to her son William, and I even wondered whether he might have emigrated, taking his mother with him. Eventually, however, I traced him in the 1901 census. Aged 40, he was living in Islington, London and working as a joiner and "wood carpenter". He was living alone but was described as married. Perhaps he was working in London for a short time, attracted by the more lucrative wages, before returning to a wife and children back in Devon. As he lay alone, far from his home, was he ever haunted by the memories of his childhood? They were memories that would never have been far from Martha's thoughts. Her story would have stayed with her, often pondered over and re-examined until perhaps with the passing of time she grew to accept that whatever she had experienced, others too had felt and will feel again and will survive. As the years went on the pain would have dulled a little, until eventually she herself died. Perhaps her story still lives on in the knowledge of her descendants, a shadowy memory passed on by her son, her grandchildren and great grandchildren.

February 1871 was a grim month in Littleham. Following the deaths in the Powe family, three children from another family also lost their lives to scarlet fever. The Molland family lived at Edge Mill, which is situated a mile from the village centre just off the Yeo Vale Road, below a terrace of cottages bearing the same name. "*Watermills in North Devon*" published by the University of the Third Age states that there are four documentary references to a Blade Mill or Edge Mill between 1563 and 1603. In 1567 it was said that there was "a bridge there called Red Bridge", though this must surely refer to Rudhabridge a short distance upstream. At that time the access to the mill would have been along a track which ran from the top of Church Lane in Littleham, joined by a now disappeared bridge over the River Yeo to another track, the remains of which can be seen on Ordnance Survey maps today, which ran up to Beaconside on the Monkleigh road. Both tracks have now partially disappeared, having become redundant when the Yeo Vale Road, a toll road, opened. *"Watermills in North Devon"* states that the mill leat ran "across the road from a pond above the cottages and discharged into the river". This stream still runs of course but is now channelled under the road. Whether this was the case in 1871 is unknown but certainly the Yeo Vale Road was open, so visitors to the mill had a choice of routes.

James Molland aged 34, described in the 1871 census as a miller and farmer, lived at Edge Mill with his 38-year-old wife Jane and their six children aged between three months and eight years. James and Jane had been born in Fremington and Westleigh respectively so had travelled seven or eight miles from their places of birth; all the children had been born in Littleham however so the family were well established in the area by 1871. They were a chapel-going family, the children's baptisms being recorded in the Bideford Circuit Wesleyan Register. It would have been a busy household with six young children to care for and only one servant, a 14-year-old housemaid to help. In addition there were all the comings and goings of the farm and the mill, which would have ground corn and cattle feed for local farmers. The family would have been well aware of the tragedies unfolding in the village that lay at a mile's distance above the wooded hills. When six-year-old William fell ill in the middle of February their fears were quickly to be realised; he died on February 10th and by then 21-month-old Arthur was already ill with scarlet fever. The day before William's funeral the youngest baby, three-month-old Rosa was baptised privately, presumably at home. Perhaps she too had contracted scarlet fever, or perhaps her parents were just fearful that she would do so and feared for her salvation should she die unbaptised. She would have received some immunity from the disease through being breast-fed; scarlet fever held more danger for young children than new babies and her mother might have kept her apart from the other children to protect her. Curiously it was the Church of England curate, James Andrew, who performed the baptism and recorded the event in the Church Register; as he lived in the village it would have been far easier to contact him in an emergency so perhaps practicality took precedence over dogma. Mr Andrew must have impressed them because subsequent children were baptised in the church.

Rosa survived this particular illness but little Arthur died two days after his brother's funeral. Their sister Ellen, aged almost three, died two weeks later. In five weeks there had been six burials of small coffins in Littleham churchyard, six children from just two families. The family had more difficult times to come. Rosa died three years later. Three further children were born, but by 1881 it was Jane who was described as head of the household at Edge Mill with her five remaining children and two servants. She was still married and I was puzzled as to James's whereabouts. After searching the census returns I found him at Devon County Lunatic Asylum in Exminster. Had the loss of his children proved too great a burden for him? Ten years later Jane, probably finding the task of running the mill and farm on her own too onerous, had moved to Bideford and was working as a launderess. She lived with her daughter Pollyann, who had been four years old at the time of the scarlet fever epidemic, and her 15-year-old son Francis. Alongside Francis's name in the census was one word. Imbecile.

We cannot know how these families were affected by the deaths of their children. Perhaps James Molland would have found his way to the asylum even if it had not been for the deaths of his children. After all not all the inhabitants of that forbidding place were traumatised by child deaths. One could follow the fortunes of many families and find downfall where there was no apparent cause. However some research has suggested that there were gender differences in the ability of parents to reach acceptance of their children's deaths, fathers finding the process more difficult than their wives. This may have been partly because women tended to be closer to the process of dying while men had to continue working. Women were also forced to accept the roles of patience, humility and obedience, although this may have been truer of middle class than working class women. Pat Jalland in *"Death in the Victorian Family"* wrote of the responses of two men to the deaths of their children: Archibald Tait who lost five children in as many weeks to scarlet fever in 1856 and Edward Benson whose son died in 1878. Both men went on to be Archbishops of Canterbury yet despite their faith found the deaths extremely difficult to come to turns with, more so than did their wives. Edward Benson said that his son's death was the "inexplicable grief" of his life and wrote "to see into that will be worth dying." How much harder it must have been for those whose faith that the family would one day be reunited was less strong.

After the deaths of the Molland children it was to be six weeks before the next death from scarlet fever. However on March 13th a child died in Mount Pleasant. When I obtained the death certificate for Mary Ann Westcott I found that the cause of death was given as "diseased brain". Research suggested that this might be a term used in the nineteenth century for severe cases of cerebral palsy, a condition that would have been poorly understood at that time. The state of medical knowledge in the nineteenth century meant that there were sometimes errors in the assumed causes of death even when certificated by a doctor. There were also many terms which are no longer in use, such as flux for dysentery and apoplexy for a cerebral haemorrhage. We cannot be sure of the real reason for Mary Ann Westcott's death. It is possible that she had caught meningitis, as it is known that William Powe, a near neighbour, had died from the disease two weeks previously. Meningitis was often known as "brain fever," not so very different in nineteenth century parlance from "diseased brain" though it would be strange if the doctor was able to diagnose it in one case but not the other. Perhaps she did suffer from cerebral palsy, a condition that can involve fits. There was no anti-epileptic medication in the nineteenth century. In 1871 the parents of a child with disabilities would not have had the access to information, guidance and assistance that families have today but perhaps the support of a large, loving family and close-knit community was as effective.

Mary Westcott lived in the larger part of the house where I now live. Until her death she shared the house with three of her six brothers and sisters and her parents William and Maria. There were also three older siblings, Elizabeth, 16, William, 18, a gardener living at Higher Winsford near Abbotsham and Caroline, 22, a kitchen maid at Yeo Vale House, a mansion a mile and a half from Littleham which has since been demolished. William and Maria had lost two other children in previous years, another Mary in 1849 and Thomas in 1853, both at the age of two years. Six surviving children out of nine.

Three days after Mary's funeral it was Mothering Sunday, a day which must have been acutely painful for Maria Westcott and other mothers in the village. It was a beautifully warm Spring day, a day for celebrations and reunions, the knowledge of which can only have added to the poignancy of their loss. No doubt Maria and William's older children returned to the family home as was the custom. Francis Kilvert wrote in his diary on that day,

"Mothering Sunday, and all the country in an upturn going out visiting. Girls and boys going home to see their mothers and taking them cakes, brothers and sisters of middle age going to see each other. It is a grand visiting day. And what a magnificent day. As I walked it was so sultry that I thought it would thunder. The sun was almost overpowering. Heavy black clouds drove up and rolled round the sky without veiling the hot sunshine, black clouds with white edges they were, looking suspiciously like thunder clouds. Against these black clouds the sunshine showed the faint delicate green and pink of the trees thickening with bursting buds."

William and Maria Westcott remained in Littleham for the rest of their lives; their shared headstone can still be seen in the churchyard. William survived Maria by nine years but spent his last years surrounded by his family. His daughter Caroline had risen from her post as kitchen maid to become a cook in Bideford but she left this job to be with her father in Mount Pleasant. Two doors away from them in one direction were his son Henry and his wife; on the other side was his youngest daughter Alice. Caroline never married for in 1901, after her father's death, she was acting as housekeeper to her younger sister Alice and her husband at an inn in Bradninch. She died in Meddon Street, Bideford at the age of 72 and was buried in Littleham churchyard. The youngest son Henry, also known as Harry, became a quarryman and lived in the village all his life. There are still some in the village who remember him and his wife Susanna.

It is possible that in the weeks between Mary Westcott's death and the next death from scarlet fever, the disease continued to ravage the village. Disturbed sleep and anxiety leave no records; a tense in-drawn breath at the first sight of a rash, the weariness in a child's cry, the tentative return of hope, these things cannot be traced unless it be in the "atmosphere" on which so many comment when entering an old house. We can only imagine the heightened fears that accompanied each new appearance of the disease now that its severity could not be doubted, its effects only too clear in the many faces clouded by grief. It may be that there were once records; in an old diary perhaps, a letter, or in the accounts of poor relief from the Board of Guardians. None have been found. The next piece of information came again from the Register of Burials.

Little Harriet Glover was the daughter of William and Lucy Glover of East Furlong Cottages. They had another daughter, Selena, who was four months old. Harriet was three when she died on April 10th, the day after Easter Sunday. Her funeral took place three days later with the curate James Andrew officiating, as he had done at all the funerals which resulted from the fever. Harriet's death certificate states that she had been ill with scarlet fever for one week and with an ulcerated throat for two weeks. The Registrar had been informed of the death by Mrs Harriet Glover, grandmother, who had been "present at the death".

Harriet Glover senior lived in a cottage on Moorehead Hill with her husband William, a shoemaker, her daughter Maryanne who was a gloveress and her 16-year-old son George, a blacksmith. William, little Harriet's father, was her oldest son and like his father, worked as a shoemaker. The Glover family had moved around, living in Wales, Landcross and Northam before coming to Littleham, but it was easy to trace their movements through the census records. It was harder to trace Lucy's family, although she had lived in Littleham all her life.

I soon discovered that Lucy's maiden name was Dennis for I found the record of her marriage to William in the parish register. One of the witnesses to the marriage was her brother C. Henry Dennis, a name that was already familiar, but the place where Lucy's father's name should have appeared was blank. I knew from the 1871 census that Lucy had been born in Littleham so I searched for her in the 1851 census for the village. There she was, with her older brother "Henery", but they were not, it seemed in the family home. Although aged only four and five they were listed as "visitors" in the household of Henry Clark, a farmer of Lower Dunn and the parish clerk. He was also puzzling. He was described as married but lived with his three children aged ten, 15 and 21. His apparently estranged wife lived in Bideford with a four-year-old son. If Lucy and Henry were only visiting Henry Clark on the day of the census, where was their real home? There were six households bearing the name of Dennis in the village, containing twenty-five individuals in all. There were one or two families that could have had two children of Lucy and Henry's age. I looked next in the 1861 census, expecting them to be found in their proper place. They were nowhere to be found. It was only later, while again studying the 1861 census that I looked at the entry for Henry Clark at Lower Dunn. He was living with three of his children, Ellin aged 20, and Henry and Lucy Clark aged 14 and 13. They had been there all along, and now Henry had, it seemed, acknowledged them as his children rather than visitors and had chosen, at least for the purposes of the census, to give them his name. It is also possible, of course, that they were orphans boarded out by the Parish and then adopted, or the children of a relative of the farmer rather than his own illegitimate children. His estranged wife was now living nearby at Middle Dunn and a note in tiny script in the census read "Farmer's Wife living separately"

The identity of Henry and Lucy's mother remained a mystery. Eventually a return to the parish registers produced a record of their baptisms. Their mother was Elizabeth Dennis, of Littleham Court at the time of the baptisms, and both children were "baseborn". A search through the census however produced at least half a dozen single or widowed individuals living in the locality named Elizabeth Dennis and of childbearing age.

Historical records, made public after a hundred years, allow prying into private lives, disclosing details which in some cases may have seemed relatively unimportant to the people concerned and perhaps even unknown to those with whom they lived; while the aspects of life which were most important to those individuals – their hopes and ambitions, their friends, the happiness or otherwise of their marriages, – remain unknown and unknowable. Newspaper reports, if they exist, tend to focus on bad news such as bankruptcy, disagreements with neighbours and criminal activities, unless the individual is in the public eye. It is worth considering what records researchers of the future will find relating to us as individuals; it is likely that in many cases they will produce a very distorted picture and will sometimes reveal details that we would prefer to keep private. I kept these thoughts in mind and made a silent apology to Henry and Lucy Dennis as I searched for the solution to their ancestry.

Details of Lucy and Henry's lives proved easier to trace than did those of their parents. It has already been seen that Lucy's marriage to William Glover appeared in the Register of Marriages for 1867. Their daughter Harriet Ann was baptised three months later, Lucy and William having followed a common nineteenth century rural tradition of marrying only after pregnancy was established. A second daughter, Selena, was born at the end of 1870. Harriet's death certificate tells us the nature and duration of her fatal illness. Strangely it is the record that is "carved in stone" that is incorrect; the headstone that marks three year old Harriet's grave states that she was eight years old, an error that probably caused her parents some distress but one that they could not, perhaps, afford to have corrected.

There was to be further grief for Lucy. Harriet's headstone bears not only her name but also that of her uncle, Charles Henry Dennis. He died on May 11th 1871, just four weeks after Harriet. The entry in the Register of Burials states "killed at Kings Cross Railway Station London accidentally". His death, coming so suddenly and unexpectedly and so soon after Harriet's, must have been a cruel blow to Lucy. He was, too, her only sibling, unusual in those days of large families. There were also half brothers and sisters but we cannot know how close she was to them. One wonders by what means the news reached Littleham, how the arrangements were made for the transportation of his body back to his home village and the funeral which took place a week later.

I was curious to know whether Henry had been merely on a visit to London or – as seemed more likely – had been working on the railway, a notoriously dangerous occupation in the nineteenth century. It seemed certain that such a death would be reported in the newspapers so I first searched the relevant issues of the *Bideford Gazette* and the *North Devon Journal* at the Local Studies Library. There was no mention of Henry, even in the deaths column. It was some time later, when in London, that I decided to visit the British Library Newspaper Library. First I searched their online catalogue to find newspapers local to the Kings Cross area and requested in advance the issues close to the relevant date. As I sat on the train that rattled and swayed its way through dark tunnels and past dreary buildings to Colindale, I imagined the awe with which Henry must have viewed London. The city then would have struck an even greater contrast with Littleham than it does today.

The reading room of the library was a large, light room with a high ceiling and tall, frosted-glass windows, lined with huge leather-topped desks with stands large enough to accommodate bound volumes of broadsheet newspapers. I went to my allotted seat and waited with some trepidation for the papers I had ordered, *the North Londoner, the St Pancras and Holburn Journal,* and *the Islington Gazette.* A reverberating clatter, not unlike an approaching goods train, made me look up from my notes to see a member of the library staff approaching with an outsized trolley bearing huge leather bound volumes which he off-loaded beside the relevant desks. They were so heavy I had to use two hands and brace myself against the desk to lift the first volume on to the stand, but my reward was immediate. In the issue of *the St Pancras and Holborn Journal* dated Saturday May 13th 1871, I found a short paragraph headed

"District Intelligence, Serious Accident on the Midland Railway. – On Tuesday, Mr Murphy and Mr Lett, house surgeons of the Royal Free Hospital, Grays Inn road, admitted Charles Henry Dennis, 24, a shunter in the employ of the Midland Railway. He was knocked down by a railway truck, which passed over his leg, and severely fractured and broke it in two places. "

The dangerous nature of work on the railway was confirmed by another report. The day after Henry's death a stableman employed by the Great Northern Railway was killed by trucks at King's Cross when crossing lines "contrary to the rules of the company."

Henry died two days after the accident on 11th May. His death certificate stated the cause of death to be a "Compound fracture of leg by a Railway Carriage." Perhaps septicaemia set in, or perhaps the break was severe enough to involve major blood vessels. The risk of death from such injuries was very real before the discovery of antibiotics.

In 1871 it would have been hard for Lucy to see beyond her grief, unable to envisage a future without her daughter and brother. Perhaps in time she was able to cherish the lives that she had shared as well as mourning their loss. Perhaps a day came when she was able to remember with pleasure the sight of little Harriet at play in the churchyard, her face upturned and smiling, her fist full of the snowdrops that grow now on her grave. Beyond that there was Lucy's future, which would include more children, a girl who perhaps resembled Harriet, a boy who bore her brother's name, for although Lucy's family was sadly depleted in 1871, it was not to remain so. By 1881 she and William had moved to Sunnyside, Bideford East. Selena was ten years old and there were three further children, William aged six, Florry, three and a two-year-old boy who had been named Charles H. after his uncle. In 1901 the family were back in Littleham, living at Little Ashridge Farm. William was now a farmer and Charles H. a carpenter.

On May 1st 1871 the curate James Andrew conducted yet another funeral, this time of two little brothers who had died on the same day, Richard and William Bailey aged two years and nine weeks respectively. They were the only sons of James and Mary Jane Bailey of Ford, Buckland Brewer. This seemed to be the farm now known as Hoopers Water, a farm technically in the parish of Buckland but lying closer to Littleham. Three daughters of seven, five and four remained. The family went on to have four more children, three more girls but only one boy, John. All were born in the parish of Buckland Brewer with the exception of one girl who, curiously, was born in born in 1877 in the United States. By the time of the 1881 census the family were living at a prestigious address in Bridgeland Street, Bideford and James

Bailey was the manager of an "Old Earthenware Pottery."

It seems the fever had left the village centre by then for there were no further deaths, but it lingered on south west of the village. In July 11-year-old Elizabeth Palmer, a near neighbour of the Baileys, died. She was the daughter of Richard and Grace Palmer, aged 45 and 48 and her home was variously described as Furlong Cottage, Higher Furlong and North Furlong. Her father was a farm labourer, no doubt at the adjoining West Furlong Farm that was run by Lewis Dennis, brother to Alexander the blacksmith. She had two brothers living in the house, three year old Charles and 19-year-old Samuel who was a railway labourer, perhaps working on the extension of the line to Torrington. Perhaps there were more cases in the Moorehead Hill area of the village in the ensuing weeks, enough to keep the fear alive in the eyes of its inhabitants.

What of George Glover, the young blacksmith? He was 16 in 1871 when his little niece, Harriet, died. He lived on Moorehead Hill with his father William, a shoemaker, his mother Harriet and his glovemaking sister, Maryanne. We do not know where he worked, but can assume it was for one of the blacksmiths in Littleham. When I think of George I prefer to picture him leaving his Moorehead home in the early dawn of a summer's morning, his shirtsleeves rolled up in preparation for the day, his mind bubbling with thoughts of work and of romance, striding up the steep tree-lined hill, across the fields and on, into his future.

# EPILOGUE

The churchyard glows in the late evening sunshine. Now there are bluebells in the long grass between the headstones, multiplying each year with careless enthusiasm. The rich reassuring murmur of a woodpigeon resounds from the old yew tree. Over there is the grave of William Powe and his daughters Elizabeth, Ellen and Mary; here Harriet Glover and her uncle, Henry Dennis. Beside them a headstone reads "In Loving Memory of George Glover, aged 16 years". A wren, its beak full of grubs, lands with cocked tail on George's stone and scrutinises the area with flirtatious glances before diving into the ivy which covers the broken headstone bearing the names of William, Arthur and Ellen Molland. I hear the high-pitched calls of young birds clamouring for their supper. The graves of the other children are unmarked, the headstones either fallen or always beyond their parents' means, but I know they are here. Further up the slope lie William and Maria Westcott, together again in restful old age; Grace Hookaway who died in 1872 aged 83. From the hedge a song thrush rejoices; the grass rustles with new life. I turn and walk slowly back along the path past the church and close the churchyard gate behind me, leaving them in peace.

# BIBLIOGRAPHY

Ascott, Major W., *Random Notes on Old Bideford and District.* (1953)

Baring Gould, S. *Devonshire Characters and Strange Events.* (1908)

Bovett, R. *Historical Notes on Devon Schools.* (1989)

Briggs, A. *A Social History of England. (1983)*

Chitty, S. *Charles Kingsley's Landscape.* (1976)

Christie, P. and Grant, A. *The Book of Bideford.* (2005)

Elihu Burritt. *Journey from London to Land's End.* (1864)

Heath, R. *The English Peasant.* (1893)

Horn, P. *Labouring Life in the Victorian Countryside.* (1976)

Horn, P. *The Victorian and Edwardian Schoolchild.* (1989)

Horn, P. *The Victorian Country Child.* (1974)

Jalland, P. *Death in the Victorian Family.* (1996)

Jefferies, R. *Hodge and His Masters. (*1880)

Jefferies, R. *The Toilers in the Field.* (1892)

Karlen, A. *Plague's Progress: A Social History of Man and Disease.* (1995)

Kilvert, F. *Journal of a Country Curate.* (1938)

Lane, J. *A Social History of Medicine.* (2001)

Malcolmson, R. and Mastoris, S. *The English Pig: A History.* (1998)

Martin, E.W. *The Shearers and the Shorn: A Study of Life in a Devon Community.* (1965)

Mingay, G.E. *A Social History of the English Countryside.* (1990)

Mingay, G.E. *Rural Life in Victorian England.* (1976)

Porter, R. *The Greatest Benefit to Mankind: A Medical History of Humanity.* (1997)

Richardson, R. *Death, Dissection and the Destitute.* (1988)

Richmond, Rev. L. *Annals of the Poor.* (1814)

Sellman, R. *Early Devon Schools.* (1984)

Sellman, R. *Devon Village Schools in the Nineteenth Century.* (1967)

Shakespeare, L. *The Memory Be Green: An Oral History of a Devon Village.* (1990)

Short, B. (Ed.) *The English Rural Community: Image and Analysis.* (1992)

Souden, D. *The Victorian Village.* (1991)

Stanes, R. *The Old Farm: A History of Farming Life in the West Country.* (1990)

Sturt, G. *A Small Boy in the Sixties.* (1927)

Sturt, G. *Change in the Village.* (1912)

Torr, C. *Small Talk at Wreyland.* (1918)

University of the Third Age. *Watermills in North Devon.* (1994)

Wood, Mrs H. *Mrs Halliburton's Troubles.* (1862)